SpringerWienNewYork

Edition Angewandte
Book Series of the University of Applied Arts Vienna

Edited by Gerald Bast, Rector

edition: 'angewandte

An envelope for arts, sciences, politics and us
Mixing realities and mediating myths & methods

Valerie Deifel, Bernd Kraeftner, Virgil Widrich (Eds.)

SpringerWienNewYork

Editors: Valerie Deifel, Bernd Kraeftner, Virgil Widrich
Art & Science, University of Applied Arts Vienna
Oskar Kokoschka-Platz 2, 1010 Vienna
www.dieangewandte.at
pr@uni-ak.ac.at

Printed in Austria
SpringerWienNewYork is a part of
Springer Science + Business Media
springer.at

Graphic Design: Pepa Bugueiro Domingo, David Palme
(envelope@agence173.com)
Copyediting: Peter Blakeney, Christine Schöffler
Printed by: Holzhausen Druck GmbH, 1140 Wien

Printed on acid-free and chlorine-free bleached paper
SPIN: 80134149

Library of Congress Control Number: 2011940163
With 98 color figures and 57 black-and-white figures

ISSN 1866-248X
ISBN 978-3-7091-0989-2 SpringerWienNewYork

An envelope for arts, sciences, politics and us
Mixing realities and mediating myths & methods

When writing a letter in the traditional - meanwhile, almost obsolete - way, there comes the point where you fold the paper and seal it in the envelope. This moment, the decision that the envelope is ready to be sealed, is crucial and sometimes it can be nerve racking. It closes the many possibilities of what to put into the package. The envelope is not part of the letter, although it announces its arrival and gives hints on what it is about. A handwritten address, a window framing the machine-typed address on the letter, a stamp that facilitates passage through the postal service, the materiality, colour, smell, and feel of the paper wrapping: It hides and reveals the inner value. The envelope serves as a temporary vessel for the more important transmitted message, and it will most likely be tossed in the waste paper basket once it has served its purpose.

The book in hand is wrapped in an envelope as well. Likewise, it is an envelope in itself, containing thoughts, images, considerations of guest speakers, and theoretical references in the immediate and broader context of establishing an Art & Science class at the University of Applied Arts Vienna. As the first master programme in accordance with the Bologna process, “Art & Science Visualization” was introduced as a study option in October 2009. The curriculum opened up the attractive promise of a think tank that mixes students from the sciences with students coming from arts and media design. However, the implementation of such a programme is not a trivial task as it involves the different ambitions and backgrounds of numerous people, including the supervising team. Initially, the curriculum focused on science visualization by means of computer graphics, which helped to narrow down the broad field to a manageable workload and professional perspective, but it also made the pursuit of the different interests of the heterogeneous student crowd more difficult. Since October 2011, the study programme has been renamed “Art & Science”, combining the core theoretical and artistic class with tutoring at other academic institutes. To account for the scientific education in an art-based programme, introductory workshops are organised in cooperation with Viennese institutes, for example, the Institute of Molecular Biotechnology (IMBA), the Medical University, or the University of Technology. The courses are held in English to attract the interest of international participants. In summary, the redesigned programme functions like a hub that coordinates different interests and research specifications, and organises cooperations with partner institutions, researchers, or artists.

An envelope for arts, sciences, politics and us combines two main sources of material: first, contributions that document the development of the Art & Science department, some of which have been compiled collectively; and second, contributions by invited guests and interesting positions that refer to a wider art/science field.

To a great extent, the production of the publication was a collective effort by the Art & Science class of 2010/2011 and its supervising team. It should portray experiences of encountering utopian thinking, unmet expectations, and bureaucratic obstacles. During this process, the most refreshing approaches and innovative sparks were found in the exchange of knowledge and the support for each other's endeavours. Some of the contributions in this publication refer to these collaborations. "16 Images of the Week" is a collection of found footage images that attracted the interest of the student contributors, which can be seen and discussed as transition zones of scientific and artistic realities. "Penser avec ~~(la chemise de)~~ Marcel" by Bernd Kraeftner et al. refers to an artwork of Marcel Broodthaers. By means of a letter and a portrait gallery, it reappropriates the methodological playfulness of the work and its inherent issues. In March 2011, the first student exhibition was organised: "parameter{world} - parameters for every or no thing". The spreads of the exhibition catalogue refer to this class project as a collection of works. In "What do you do?" Virgil Widrich, head of the department, provides a survey of the ongoing projects and their diversity as a response to this inevitable question. Finally, the

"Gorilla Manifesto" compiles statements of the students on their wishes and thoughts regarding collaborations between arts and sciences.

Complementing these "collaborative" contributions from the department, the words of guest speakers establish new relationships and plot a map of greater fields of interest. Excerpts from encounters with Thomas Bugnyar, Valérie Pihet, Nikolaus Gansterer, Victoria Vesna, and Oron Catts present fragments of their work about the application of different methods and how to handle funding and organisational restraints in different research/artistic communities. Art as research, research as art, anything goes? In the past years, there have been a lot of comparable efforts to breathe life into the matter of artistic research. Beside the projects of Victoria Vesna (Art|Sci Center, UCLA) and Oron Catts (SymbioticA, University of Western Australia), Tom Holert, for instance, has established - and not so far away from the University of Applied Arts geographically - a "Center for Art/Knowledge" and the transdisciplinary PhD programme "PhD in Practice" at the Academy of Fine Arts Vienna. Johanna Schaffer, also co-leader with Holert of the collaborative research project "Troubling Research", refers in her slightly polemic assessment of "Artistic Re-re-research" to the politics of artistic research, the institutional setup, and the development of this PhD programme. The master programme "Experiments in Arts and Politics", initiated by Bruno Latour and implemented by Valérie Pihet at Sciences Po, Paris, in October 2010, represents another position in the art/science field. In the programme, (social) scientists mix with artists, and they are confronted with and involved in specific societal constellations and political issues. Latour, in his essay "An Attempt at a 'Compositionist Manifesto'", elucidates the philosophy behind this one-year master course. Furthermore, Tom Holert's "Joint Ventures" reflects on the subversive reading of collective endeavours through a historical perspective and points out how collaborative practices in the arts can be considered as incubators of intellectual and economic independence. However, this independence may also come along with the problem of authorship and clear cut positioning on the professional art market.

The book is opened and closed by manifestos, highlighting an "outmoded genre in the grand style of old" (→Latour, 16). The main goal in writing a manifesto is to summon desired prospects. Nevertheless, it also builds very much on that what is already factual and explicit in order to reach out to these new potentials. As a manifesto that attempts to invoke more than just a couple of assumptions, its words are formulated, at best, to prompt movement and change in the world, which involves the performative quality of actual doing. *"Permanent process of rethinking embedded in the chance of redoing. Sophisticated, freedom-based, and advanced field of study. Many layers and several directions to move. Multiple fields of research."* (→*Gorilla Manifesto*, 231)

The editors
Vienna, 2 September 2011

Bruno Latour An Attempt at a "Compositionist Manifesto"

For D. H.

Latour, Bruno. An Attempt at a "Compositionist Manifesto".
New Literary History 41:3 (2010), 471–490.

A prologue in the form of an avatar

If I had an agent, I am sure he would advise me to sue James Cameron over his latest blockbuster since *Avatar* should really be called *Pandora's Hope*![1] Yes, Pandora is the name of the mythical humanoid figure whose box holds all the ills of humanity, but it is also the name of the heavenly body that humans from planet Earth (all members of the typically American military-industrial complex) are exploiting to death without any worry for the fate of its local inhabitants, the Navis, and their ecosystem, a superorganism and goddess called Eywa. I am under the impression that this film is the first popular description of what happens when modernist humans meet Gaia. And it's not pretty.

The *Revenge of Gaia*, to draw on the title of a book by James Lovelock, results in a terrifying replay of Dunkirk 1940 or Saigon 1973: a retreat and a defeat.[2] This time, the Cowboys lose to the Indians: they have to flee from their frontier and withdraw back home abandoning all their riches behind them. In trying to pry open the mysterious planet Pandora in search of a mineral—known as unobtanium, no less!—the Earthlings, just as in the classical myth, let loose all the ills of humanity: not only do they ravage the planet, destroy the great tree of life, and kill the quasi-Amazonian Indians who had lived in edenic harmony with it, but they also become infected with their own macho ideology. Outward destruction breeds inward destruction. And again, as in the classical myth, hope is left at the bottom of Pandora's box—I mean planet—because it lies deep in the forest, thoroughly hidden in the complex web of connections that the Navis nurture with their own Gaia, a biological and cultural network which only a small team of naturalists and anthropologists are beginning to explore.[3] It is left to Jake, an outcast, a marine with neither legs nor academic credentials, to finally "get it," yet at a price: the betrayal of his fellow mercenaries, a rather conventional love affair with a native, and a magnificent transmigration of his original crippled body into his avatar, thereby inverting the relationship between the original and the copy and giving a whole new dimension to what it means to "go native".

I take this film to be the first Hollywood script about the modernist clash with nature that doesn't take ultimate catastrophe and destruction for granted—as so many have before—but opts for a much more interesting outcome: a new search for hope on condition that what it means to have a body, a mind, and a world is completely redefined. The lesson of the film, in my reading of it, is that modernized and modernizing humans are not physically, psychologically, scientifically, and emotionally equipped to survive on their planet. As in Michel Tournier's inverted story of Robinson Crusoe, *Friday, or, The Other Island*, they have to relearn from beginning to end what it is to live on their island—and just like Tournier's fable, Crusoe ultimately decides to stay in the now civilized and civilizing jungle instead of going back home to what for him has become just another wilderness.[4] But what fifty years ago in Tournier's romance was a fully *individual* experience has become today in Cameron's film a *collective* adventure: there is no sustainable life for Earth-bound species on their planet island.

Why write a manifesto?

It is in the dramatic atmosphere induced by Cameron's opera that I want to write a draft of my manifesto. I know full well that, just like the time of avant-gardes or that of the Great Frontier, the time of manifestos has long passed. Actually, it is the time of *time* that has passed: this strange idea of a vast army moving forward, preceded by the most daring innovators and thinkers, followed by a mass of slower and heavier crowds, while the rearguard of the most archaic, the most primitive, the most reactionary people, trails behind—just like the Navis, trying hopelessly to slow down the inevitable charge forward. During this recently defunct time of time, manifestos were like so many war cries intended to speed up the movement, ridicule the Philistines, castigate the reactionaries.

This huge war-like narrative was predicated on the idea that the flow of time had one—and only one—*inevitable* and *irreversible* direction. The war waged by the avant-gardes would be won, no matter how many defeats they suffered. What this series of manifestos pointed to was the inevitable march of *progress*. So much so that these manifestos could be used like so many signposts to decide who was more "progressive" and who was more "reactionary".

Today, the avant-gardes have all but disappeared, the front line is as impossible to draw as the precise boundaries of terrorist networks, and the well-arrayed labels "archaic", "reactionary", and "progressive" seem to hover haphazardly like a cloud of mosquitoes. If there is one thing that has vanished, it is the idea of a flow of time moving inevitably and irreversibly forward that can be predicted by clear-sighted thinkers. The spirit of the age, if there is such a *Zeitgeist*, is rather that everything that had been taken for granted in the modernist grand narrative of Progress is fully *reversible* and that it is impossible to trust in the clearsightedness of anyone—especially academics. If we needed a proof of that (un) fortunate state of affairs, a look at the recent 2009 Climate Summit in Copenhagen would be enough: at the same time that some, like James Lovelock, argued that human civilization itself is threatened by the "revenge of Gaia" (a good case if any, as we will see later, of a fully reversible flow of time!), the greatest assembly of representatives of the human race managed to sit on their hands for days doing nothing and making no decisions whatsoever. Whom are we supposed to believe: those who say climate change is a life-threatening event? Those who, by doing nothing much, state that it can be handled by business as usual? or those who say that the march of progress should go on, no matter what?

And yet a manifesto might not be so useless at this point, making explicit (that is, *manifest*) a subtle but radical transformation in the definition of what it means to progress, that is, to *process* forward and meet new prospects. Not as a war cry for an avant-garde to move even further and faster ahead, but rather as a warning, a call to attention, so as to *stop* going further *in the same way* as before toward the future.[5] The nuance I want to outline is that between *progress* and *progressive*. It is as if we had to move from an idea of inevitable progress to one of *tentative and precautionary progression*. There is still a movement. Something is still going forward. But, as I will explain in the third section, the tenor is entirely different. And since it seems impossible to draft a manifesto without a word ending with an "–ism" (communism, futurism, surrealism, situationism, etc.), I have chosen to give this manifesto a worthy banner, the word *compositionism*. Yes, I would like to be able to write "The Compositionist Manifesto" by reverting to an outmoded genre in the grand style of old, beginning with something like: "A specter haunts not only Europe but the world: that of compositionism. All the Powers of the Modernist World have entered into a holy alliance to exorcise this specter!"

Even though the word "composition" is a bit too long and windy, what is nice is that it underlines that things have to be put together (Latin *componere*) while retaining their heterogeneity. Also, it is connected with composure; it has clear roots in art, painting, music, theater, dance, and thus is associated with choreography and scenography; it is not too far from "compromise" and "compromising", retaining a certain diplomatic and prudential flavor. Speaking of flavor, it carries with it the pungent but ecologically correct smell of "compost", itself due to the active "de-composition" of many invisible agents....[6] Above all, a composition can *fail* and thus retains what is most important in the notion of *constructivism* (a label which I could have used as well, had it not been already taken by art history). It thus draws attention away from the irrelevant difference between what is constructed and what is not constructed, toward the crucial difference between what is *well* or *badly* constructed, *well* or *badly* composed.[7] What is to be composed may, at any point, be *de*composed.

In other words, compositionism takes up the task of searching for universality but without believing that this universality is already there, waiting to be unveiled and discovered. It is thus as far from relativism (in the papal sense of the word) as it is from universalism (in the modernist meaning of the world—more on this later). From universalism it takes up the task of building a common world; from relativism, the certainty that this common world has to be built from utterly heterogeneous parts that will never make a whole, but at best a fragile, revisable, and diverse composite material.

I am not going to go through all the points that would be necessary to establish the credentials of the little word compositionism. I will simply outline three successive connotations I'd like to associate with this neologism: first, by contrasting it with critique;[8] second, by exploring why it could offer a successor to nature; and lastly, since Grand Narratives are a necessary component of manifestos, in what sort of big story it could situate itself. Let's imagine that these are the first three planks of my political platform!

An alternative to critique?

In a first meaning, compositionism could stand as an alternative to *critique* (I don't mean a critique of critique but a reuse of critique; not an even more critical critique but rather critique acquired secondhand—so to speak—and put to a different use). To be sure, critique did a wonderful job of debunking prejudices, enlightening nations, and prodding minds, but, as I have argued elsewhere, it "ran out of steam" because it was predicated on the discovery of a true world of realities lying behind a veil of appearances.[9] This beautiful staging had the great advantage of creating a huge difference of potential between the world of delusion and the world of reality, thus generating an immense source of productive energy that in a few centuries reshaped the face of the Earth. But it also had the immense drawback of creating a massive gap between what was felt and what was real. Ironically, given the Nietzschean fervor of so many iconoclasts, critique relies on a rear world of the beyond, that is, on a transcendence that is no less transcendent for being fully secular. With critique, you may debunk, reveal, unveil, but only as long as you establish, through this process of creative destruction, a privileged access to the world of reality behind the veils of appearances. Critique, in other words, has all the limits of utopia: it relies on the certainty of the world *beyond* this world. By contrast, for compositionism, there is no world of beyond. It is all about *immanence*.

The difference is not moot, because *what performs a critique cannot also compose*. It is really a mundane question of having the right tools for the right job. With a hammer (or a sledge hammer) in hand you can do a lot of things: break down walls, destroy idols, ridicule prejudices, but you cannot repair, take care, assemble, reassemble, stitch together. It is no more possible to compose with the paraphernalia of critique than it is to cook with a seesaw. Its limitations are greater still, for the hammer of critique can only prevail if, behind the slowly dismantled wall of appearances, is finally revealed the netherworld of reality. But when there is nothing real to be seen behind this destroyed wall, critique suddenly looks like another call to nihilism. What is the use of poking holes in delusions, if nothing more true is revealed beneath?

This is precisely what has happened to postmodernism, which can be defined as another form of modernism, fully equipped with the same iconoclastic tools as the moderns, but without the belief in a real world beyond. No wonder it had no other solution but to break itself to pieces, ending up debunking the debunkers. Critique was meaningful only as long as it was accompanied by the sturdy yet juvenile belief in a real world beyond. Once deprived of this naïve belief in transcendence, critique is no longer able to produce this difference of potential that had literally given it steam. As if the hammer had ricocheted off the wall and smashed the debunkers. And this is why it has been necessary to move from iconoclasm to what I have called *iconoclash*—namely, the *suspension* of the critical impulse, the transformation of debunking from a *resource* (the main resource of intellectual life in the last century, it would seem) to a *topic* to be carefully studied.[10] While critics still believe that there is too much belief and too many things standing in the way of reality, compositionists believe that there are enough ruins and that everything has to be reassembled piece by piece. Which is another way of saying that we don't wish to have too much to do with the twentieth century: "Let the dead bury their dead."

In suspending the critical gesture, we begin to understand retrospectively the oddness of the definition of nature to which critique had been wed. It had two surprising features: the discovery, revelation, unveiling of what lay behind the subjective fog of appearances; and what ensured the continuity in space and time of all beings in their inner reality. It has long been realized by science studies, by feminist theory, and, in a much wider way, by all sorts of environmental movements, that this era's character was precisely not the long-awaited taking into account of nature, but rather the total dissolution of the various notions of nature. In brief, ecology seals the end of nature.

Even though the word "postnatural" has begun to pop up (for instance in Erle Ellis's "postnatural environmentalism"),[11] compositionism would probably be more comfortable with the words "pre-naturalism" or "multinaturalism".[12] Nature is not a thing, a domain, a realm, an ontological territory. It is (or rather, it was during the short modern parenthesis) a way of organizing the division (what Alfred North Whitehead has called the Bifurcation)[13] between appearances and reality, subjectivity and objectivity, history and immutability. A fully transcendent, yet a fully historical construct, a deeply religious way (but not in the truly religious sense of the word)[14] of creating the difference of potential between what human souls were attached to and what was really out there. And also, as I have shown elsewhere, a fully *political* way of distributing power in what I have called the Modernist Constitution, a sort of unwritten compact between what could be and what could not be *discussed.*[15] Once you begin to trace an absolute distinction between what is deaf and dumb and who is allowed to speak, you can easily imagine that this is not an ideal way to establish some sort of democracy.... But no doubt that it is a fabulously useful ploy, invented in the seventeenth century, to establish a political epistemology and to decide who will be allowed to talk about what, and which types of beings will remain silent. This was the time of the great political, religious, legal, and epistemological invention of *matters of fact*, embedded in a *res extensa* devoid of any meaning, except that of being the ultimate reality, made of fully silent entities that were yet able, through the mysterious intervention of Science (capital S) to "speak by themselves" (but without the mediation of science, small s, and scientists—also small s!).

This whole modernist mise-en-scène now appears to be the queerest anthropological construction, especially because Progress, under the label of Reason, was defined as the quick substitution of this odd nature for subjective, local, cultural, and human, all too human, values. The idea was that the more natural we became, the more rational we would be, and the easier the agreements between all reasonable human beings. (Remember the big bulldozers and warships of *Avatar* in their irreversible—in fact, fully reversible—advance to destroy the great tree of life?) This agreement now lies in ruins, but without having been superseded by another more realistic and especially more livable project. In this sense, we are still postmodern.

A successor to Nature?

This is precisely the point where compositionism wishes to take over: *what is the successor of nature?* Of course, no human, no atom, no virus, no organism has ever resided "in" nature understood as *res extensa*. They have all lived in the pluriverse, to use William James's expression—where else could they have found their abode? As soon as the Bifurcation was invented at the time of Descartes and Locke, it was immediately undone. No composition has ever been so fiercely decomposed. Remember: "We have never been modern"—so this utopia of nature has always been just that, a utopia, a world of beyond without any realistic handle on the practice of science, technology, commerce, industry.

And yet it has retained an enormous power over the political epistemology of the Moderns. Not a power of description, of course, not a power of explanation, but the power to create this very difference of potential that has given critique its steam and modernism its impetus. So the question now, for those who wish to inherit from modernism without being postmodern (as is my own case, at least), is what it is to live *without* this difference of potential? Where will we get the energy to act without such a gigantic steam engine? Where will compositionism draw its steam? What would it mean to move forward without this engine? And to move collectively, that is, billions of people and their trillions of affiliates and commensals?

Such a total disconnect between the ruins of naturalism, on the one hand, and the slow and painful emergence of its successor on the other, is exemplified in the funny bout of agitation which started just before the Climate Summit (non)event in Copenhagen, around what has been called "climategate".[16] It is a trivial example, but so revealing of the tasks at hand for those who wish to shift from a nature always already there to an assemblage to be slowly composed.

In the fall of 2009, critics and proponents of anthropogenic climate change realized, by sifting through the thousands of emails of climate scientists stolen by activists of dubious pedigree, that the scientific facts of the matter had to be *constructed*, and by whom? By humans! Squabbling humans assembling data, refining instruments to make the climate speak (instruments! can you believe that!), and spotty data sets (data sets! imagine that…), and these scientists had money problems (grants!), and they had to massage, write, correct, and rewrite humble texts and articles (what? texts to be written? is science really made of texts, how shocking!).... What I found so ironic in the hysterical reactions of scientists and the press was the almost complete agreement of both opponents and proponents of the anthropogenic origin of climate change. They all seem to share the same idealistic view of Science (capital S): "If it slowly composed, it cannot be true," said the skeptics; "if we reveal how it is composed," said the proponents, "it will be discussed, thus disputable, thus it cannot be true either!"

After thirty years or so of work in science studies, it is more than embarrassing to see that scientists had no better epistemology with which to rebut their adversaries. They kept using the old opposition between what is constructed and what is not constructed, instead of the slight but crucial difference between what is *well* and what is *badly* constructed (or composed). And this pseudo-"revelation" was made at the very moment when the *disputability* of the most important tenets of what it means for billions of humans, represented by their heads of states, to live collectively on the planet was fully visible in the vast pandemonium of the biggest diplomatic jamboree ever assembled.... This was the ideal moment to connect the *disputability* of politics with the *disputability* of science (small s)—instead of trying to maintain, despite the evidence to the contrary, the usual gap between, on the one hand, what is politics and can be discussed, and, on the other hand, a Science of what is "beyond dispute".

Clearly, when faced with the "stunning revelations" of "climategate", it is not enough for us to rejoice in the discovery of the humble *human* or *social* dimension of scientific practice. Such an attitude would simply show a belief in the debunking capacity of critique, as if the thankless endeavor of scientists had to be contrasted with the pure realm of unmediated and indisputable facts. We compositionists want immanence *and* truth together. Or, to use my language: we want *matters of concern*, not only *matters of fact*. For a compositionist, nothing is beyond dispute. And yet, closure has to be achieved. But it is achieved only by the slow process of composition and compromise, not by the revelation of the world of beyond.

Just before Copenhagen, the French philosopher Michel Serres wrote a rather telling piece in the newspaper *Libération* summarizing the argument he had made, many years ago and before everyone else, in his *Natural Contract*. The article was titled "*la non-invitée au sommet de Copenhague*" or, roughly translated, "who wasn't invited to Copenhagen?"[17] Serres's piece pointed to the one empty seat at Copenhagen's Parliament of Things: that of Gaia. He wondered how to make it possible for her to sit and speak and be represented.

Unfortunately, Serres's solution was to take the language, rituals, and practices of politics—good at representing humans—and the language, procedures, and rituals of science—good at representing facts—and *join them together*. But this is easier said than done. What he dreamed of (much like Hans Jonas, earlier in the twentieth century) was in effect a government of scientists—a modernist dream, if anything—able to speak both languages at once. A very French temptation, from the "*gouvernement des savants*" during the Revolution all the way to our atomic program and our love affair with the "*corps techniques de l'Etat*", the close-knit clique of engineers-cum-bureaucrats that oversee national scientific and industrial policy. But since these two traditions of speech remain the heirs of the great Bifurcation, we have not moved an inch. For we have simply conjoined the worst of politics and the worst of science, that is, the two traditional ways of producing indisputability. We have been here already. This was once the dream of Marxism, just as it is now the dream (albeit in tatters) of run-of-the-mill economists: a science of politics instead of the total transformation of what it means to do politics (so as to include nonhumans) and what it means to do science (so as to include entangled and controversial and highly disputable matters of concern).[18] To believe in this "*gouvernement des savants*" has been precisely the mistake made by so many environmentalists when they interpreted the present crisis as the great Comeback instead of the End of Nature. *Between belief in Nature and belief in politics*, one has to choose.

Needless to say, the Copenhagen event was, in this respect, a total (and largely predictable) failure. Not because there is as yet no World Government able to enforce decisions—in the unlikely case that any had been made—but because we have as yet no idea of what it means to govern the world now that Nature as an organizing concept (or, rather, conceit) is gone. We can't live on planet Earth nor can we live on Pandora.... But one thing is sure—and "climategate" is a good case in point—it is utterly impossible to find any further use for the separation between science and politics invented by the Moderns—even by conjoining them. Two artificial constructions put together make for a *third* artificial contrivance, not for a solution to a problem that was very consciously rendered insoluble at the birth of the seventeenth century—somewhere between Thomas Hobbes and Robert Boyle, to point out a *locus classicus* of our history of science.[19] Since Nature was invented to render politics impotent, there is no reason why a politics *of Nature* would ever deliver its promises.

Back to the sixteenth century?

Because of the slow demise of Nature, I now have the feeling, much like Stephen Toulmin,[20] that we are actually closer to the sixteenth century than to the twentieth, precisely because the agreement that created the Bifurcation in the first place now lies in ruin and has to be entirely recomposed. This is why we seem to experience a sense of familiarity with the times *before* its invention and implementation.[21] When rationalists deride the time before the "epistemological break", to use Louis Althusser's favorite (and fully modernist) expression, it is because this earlier "episteme" was making too many connections between what they called the micro- and the macrocosm. But is this not exactly what we now see emerging everywhere under the name of "postnatural"? The destiny of all the cosmos—or rather *kosmoi*—is fully interconnected now that, through our very progress and through our proliferating numbers, we have taken the Earth on our shoulder—as is made so clear by the striking neologism "Anthropocene", this newly named geological era that kicked off with the Industrial Revolution and its global consequences.

Of course, what is entirely lost today is the notion of a *harmony* between the micro- and macrocosm. Yet, that there is, and that there should be, a *connection* between the fates of these two spheres seems obvious to all. Even the strange Renaissance notion of sympathy and antipathy between entities has taken an entirely new flavor now that animals, plants, soils, and chemicals are indeed acknowledged to have their friends and their enemies, their assemblies and their web sites, their blogs and their demonstrators. When naturalists introduced the word "biodiversity", they had no idea that a few decades later they would have to add to the proliferation of surprising connections among organisms the proliferation of many more surprising connections between political institutions devoted to the protection of this or that organism. While naturalists could previously limit themselves, for instance, to situating the red tuna in the great chain of predators and prey, they now have to add to this ecosystem Japanese consumers, activists, and even President Sarkozy, who had promised to protect the fish before retreating once again when confronted with the Mediterranean fishing fleet. I have this odd feeling that the new red tuna, whose territory now extends to the sushi bars of the whole planet and whose ecosystem now include friends and enemies of many human shapes, closely resembles the strange and complex emblems that were accumulated during the Renaissance in cabinets of curiosities. The order is gone, to be sure, and so is the dense and agreed upon set of allusions and metaphors from Antiquity, but the thirst for mixed connections is the same. Once again, our age has become the age of wonder at the *disorders* of nature.[22]

Four centuries later, micro- and macrocosm are now *literally* and not simply symbolically connected, and the result is a *kakosmos*, that is, in polite Greek, a horrible and disgusting mess! And yet a kakosmos is a cosmos nonetheless.... At any rate, it certainly no longer resembles the Bifurcated nature of the recent past where primary qualities (real, speechless, yet somehow speaking by themselves, but alas, devoid of any meaning and any value) went one way, while secondary qualities (subjective, meaningful, able to talk, full of values, but, alas, empty of any reality) went another. In that sense, we seem to be much closer than ever to the time before the famous "epistemological break"—a radical divide that has always been thought but never actually practiced.[23] When Alexandre Koyré wrote *From the Closed Word to the Infinite Universe*,[24] little could he predict that barely half a century later the "Infinite Universe" would have become an entangled pluriverse all over again!

But there is no way to devise a successor to nature, if we do not tackle the tricky question of *animism* anew.[25] One of the principal causes of the scorn poured by the Moderns on the sixteenth century is that those poor archaic folks, who had the misfortune of living on the wrong side of the "epistemological break," believed in a world *animated* by all sorts of entities and forces instead of believing, like any rational person, in an *inanimate* matter producing its effects only through the power of its causes. It is this conceit that lies at the root of all the critiques of environmentalists as being too "anthropocentric" because they dare to "attribute" values, price, agency, purpose to what cannot have and should not have any intrinsic value (lions, whales, viruses, CO_2, monkeys, the ecosystem, or, worst of all, Gaia). The accusation of anthropomorphism is so strong that it paralyzes all the efforts of many scientists in many fields—but especially biology—to go beyond the narrow constraints of what is believed to be "materialism" or "reductionism". It immediately gives a sort of New Age flavor to any such efforts, as if the default position were the idea of the inanimate and the bizarre innovation were the animate. Add agency? You must be either mad or definitely marginal. Consider Lovelock, for instance, with his "absurd idea" of the Earth as a quasi-organism—or the Navis with their "prescientific" connections to Eywa.[26]

But what should appear extraordinarily bizarre is, on the contrary, the invention of *inanimate* entities which do nothing more than carry *one step further* the cause that makes them act to generate an n+1 outcome, which is in turn nothing but the cause of an n+2 outcome. This conceit has the strange result of composing the world out of long concatenations of cause and effect where (this is what is so odd) *nothing is supposed to happen*, except, probably at the beginning—but since there is no God in these staunchly secular accounts, there is not even a beginning.... The disappearance of agency in the so-called "materialist world view" is a stunning invention, especially since it is contradicted every step of the way by the odd resistance of reality: every consequence adds slightly to a cause. Thus, it has to have some sort of agency. There is a supplement, a gap between the two. If not, there would be no possible way of discriminating causes from consequences. This is true in particle physics as well as in chemistry, biology, psychology, economics, or sociology.

Thus, although in practice all agencies have to be distributed at each step of the whole concatenation, in theory nothing goes on but the strict and unaltered transportation of a cause.[27] To use my technical language, although every state of affairs deploys associations of *mediators*, everything is supposed to happen as if only chains of purely passive *intermediaries* were to unfold.[28] Paradoxically, the most stubborn realism, the most rational outlook is predicated on the most unrealistic, the most contradictory notion of an *action without agency*.

How could such a contradictory metaphysics have the slightest bearing on our ways of thinking? Because it has the great advantage of ensuring the *continuity* of space and time by connecting all entities through concatenations of causes and consequences. Thus, for this assembly *no composition is necessary*. In such a conception, nature is *always already assembled*, since nothing happens but what comes from before. It is enough to have the causes, the consequences will follow, and they will possess nothing of their own except the carrying further of the same indisputable set of characteristics. Let these automatic causal chains do their work and they will build up the cage of nature. Anyone who denies their existence, who introduces discontinuities, who lets agency proliferate by pointing out many interesting gaps between causes and consequences, will be considered a deviant, a mad man, a dreamer—in any event, not a rational being.

If there is one thing to wonder about in the history of Modernism, it is not that there are still people "mad enough to believe in animism", but that so many hardheaded thinkers have invented what should be called *inanimism* and have tied to this sheer impossibility their definition of what it is to be "rational" and "scientific". It is inanimism that is the queer invention: an agency without agency constantly denied by practice.

This is what lies at the heart of the Modernist Constitution. And as Philippe Descola has so nicely shown, what makes it even odder is that this inanimism (he calls it naturalism) is *the most anthropocentric* of all the modes of relation invented, across the world, to deal with associations between humans and nonhumans.[29] All the others are trying to underline agency as much as possible at each step. They might often seem odd in their definition of agency—at least to us—but if there is one thing they never do, it is to *deny the gap* between causes and consequences or to circumscribe agency by limiting it to human subjectivity. For the three other modes discussed by Descola, namely animism, totemism, and analogism, the proliferation of agencies is precisely what does *not* introduce any difference between humans and nonhumans.

This is why rationalists never detect the contradiction between what they say about the continuity of causes and consequences and what they witness—namely the discontinuity, invention, supplementarity, creativity ("creativity is the ultimate" as Whitehead said[30]) between associations of mediators. They simply transform this discrepancy (which would make their worldview untenable) into a radical divide between human subjects and nonhuman objects. For purely anthropocentric—that is, political—reasons, naturalists have built their collective to make sure that subjects and objects, culture and nature remain utterly distinct, with only the former having any sort of agency. An extraordinary feat: making, for purely anthropocentric reasons, the accusation of being anthropomorphic into a deadly weapon! In the fight to establish the continuity of space and time without having to compose it, it has been the most anthropomorphic individuals who have succeeded in rejecting all the others for practicing the most horrible, archaic, dangerous, and reactionary forms of animism.

Although this might seem too technical a point, it is important not to confuse such an argument with the plea *against* reductionism with which it is in great danger of being confused. In all disciplines, reductionism offers an enormously *useful* handle to allow scientists to insert their instrumentarium, their paradigms, and to produce long series of practical effects—often entire industries as is the case with biotechnology.[31] But success at handling entities by generating results and entire industries out of them is not the same thing as building the cage of nature with its long chains of causes and consequences. It is actually the opposite: what reductionism shows in practice is that only the proliferation of ingenious detours, of highly localized sets of skills, is able to extract interesting and useful results from a multitude of agencies.[32] Consider how fabulously useful the "Central Dogma" of the first versions of

DNA was in beginning to unlock the power of genes: and yet no active biologists now believe that these earlier versions could be of any use for building the "naturalistic" definition of what it is for an organism to live in the real world.[33] There is a complete—and continuously growing—disconnect between efficient handles and the staging of nature. Once you put to one side this proliferation of clever skills, you are not defining the nature of things, you simply enter into something else entirely: the spurious continuity of nature. And the same thing could be shown every time you move from reductionist handles to reductionism as a philosophical—that is, a political—worldview.

Compositionists, however, cannot rely on such a solution. The continuity of all agents in space and time *is not given to them* as it was to naturalists: they have to compose it, slowly and progressively. And, moreover, to compose it from discontinuous pieces. Not only because human destiny (microcosm) and nonhuman destiny (macrocosm) are now entangled for everyone to see (contrary to the strange dream of Bifurcation), but for a much deeper reason on which the capture of the creativity of all agencies depends: consequences overwhelm their causes, and this overflow has to be respected everywhere, in every domain, in every discipline, and for every type of entity. It is no longer possible to build the cage of nature—and indeed it has never been possible to live in this cage. This is, after all, what is meant by the *eikos* of ecology.[34] Call it "animism" if you wish, but it will no longer be enough to brand it with the mark of infamy. This is indeed why we feel so close to the sixteenth century, as if we were back before the "epistemological break", before the odd invention of matter (a highly idealist construct as Whitehead has shown so well).[35] As science studies and feminist theory have documented over and over again, the notion of matter is too political, too anthropomorphic, too narrowly historical, too ethnocentric, too gendered, to be able to define the stuff out of which the poor human race, expelled from Modernism, has to build its abode. We need to have a much more material, much more mundane, much more immanent, much more realistic, much more embodied definition of the material world if we wish to compose a common world.

There is also a reason that would have seemed important in the sixteenth century but which is a hallmark of our own—namely the proliferation of scientific controversies. This is a well-known phenomenon, but it is still vital to emphasize it at this juncture: what makes it impossible to continue to rely on the continuity of space and time implied in the notion of nature and its indisputable chains of causes and consequences is the foregrounding of so many controversies *inside* the sciences themselves. Once again this phenomenon is lamented by rationalists who still wish to paint science as capable of producing incontrovertible, indisputable, mouth-shutting matters of fact. But, if I dare say so, the fact of the matter is that matters of fact are in great risk of disappearing, like so many other endangered species. Or else they deal with trifling subjects of no interest to anyone anymore. Rare now are topics where you do not see scientists publicly disagreeing among themselves on what they are, how they should be studied, financed, portrayed, distributed, understood, cast. Facts have become *issues*.[36] And the more important the issue, the less certain we are now publicly as to how to handle it (think of the fracas around the H1N1 influenza virus in 2009, or "climategate"). And this is good.... at least for compositionists, since it now adds a third source of discontinuity forcing all of us—scientists, activists, and politicians alike—to compose the common world from disjointed pieces instead of taking for granted that the unity, continuity, agreement is already there, embedded in the idea that "the same nature fits all". The increase of disputability—and the amazing extension of scientific and technical controversies—while somewhat terrifying at first, is also the best path to finally taking seriously the political task of establishing the continuity of all entities that make up the common world.[37] I hope to have made it clear why I stated earlier that between nature and politics one has to choose, and why what is to be critiqued cannot be composed.

No future but many prospects?

Critique, nature, progress: three of the ingredients of Modernism that have to be decomposed before being recomposed. I have had a quick look at the first two. What about the third, namely, progress? I want to argue that there might have been some misunderstanding, during the Modernist parenthesis, about the very direction of the flow of time. I have this strange fantasy that the modernist hero never actually looked toward the future but always *to the past*, the archaic past that he was fleeing in terror.

I don't wish to embrace Walter Benjamin's tired "Angel of History" trope, but there is something right in the position he attributed to the angel: it looks backward and not ahead. "Where *we* see the appearance of a chain of events, *he* sees one single catastrophe, which unceasingly piles rubble on top of rubble and hurls it before his feet."[38] But contrary to Benjamin's interpretation, the Modern who, like the angel, is flying backward[39] is actually *not seeing the destruction*; He is generating it in his flight since it occurs behind His back! It is only recently, by a sudden conversion, a *metanoia* of sorts, that He has suddenly realized how much catastrophe His development has left behind him. The ecological crisis is nothing but the sudden *turning* around of someone who had actually *never before* looked into the future, so busy was He extricating Himself from a horrible past.[40] There is something Oedipal in this hero fleeing His past so fiercely that He cannot realize—except too late—that it is precisely His flight that has created the destruction He was trying to avoid in the first place. Oedipus, pursued by *dikè*, the Fate who reigns even over the gods, was tragic. But with the Moderns there is no god and thus no tragedy to expect. Simply a gigantic, myopic, bloody, and sometimes comical blunder—just like the botched attack of the "people from the Sky" against Eywa. I want to argue that Moderns had never contemplated their future, until a few years back! They were too busy fleeing their past in terror. A great advance would be made in their anthropology, if we were able to discover what horror they were escaping that gave them so much energy to flee.[41] What the Moderns called "their future" has never been contemplated face to face, since it has always been the future of someone fleeing their past looking *backward*, not *forward*. This is why, as I emphasized earlier, their future was always so unrealistic, so utopian, so full of hype.

The French language, for once richer than English, differentiates "*le futur*" from "*l'avenir*". In French, I could say that the Moderns had "*un futur*" but never "*un avenir*". To define the present situation, I have to translate and say that the Moderns always had a future (the odd utopian future of someone fleeing His past in reverse!) but never a chance, until recently that is, to turn to what I could call their *prospect*: the shape of things to come. As it is now clear from the ecological crisis, one's future and one's prospect (if one takes on board these two words) bear almost no resemblance to one another.[42] What makes the times we are living in so interesting (and why I still think it is useful to make this manifest through a manifesto) is that we are progressively discovering that, just at the time when people are despairing at realizing that they might, in the end, have "no future", we suddenly have many *prospects*. Yet they are so utterly different from what we imagined *while fleeing ahead looking backwards* that we might cast them only as so many fragile illusions. Or find them even more terrifying than what we were trying to escape from.

Faced with those new prospects, the first reaction is to do nothing. There is a strong, ever so modernist, temptation to exclaim: "Let's flee as before and *have our past future back*!" instead of saying: "Let's stop fleeing, *break for good* with our future, turn our back, *finally*, to our past, and explore our new prospects, what lies ahead, the fate of things to come." Is this not exactly what the fable of the crippled Jake abandoning his body for his avatar is telling us: instead of a future of no future, why not try to see if we could not have a prospect at last? After three centuries of Modernism, it is not asking too much from those who, in practice, have never managed to be Moderns, to finally *look ahead*.

Of course, what they see is not pretty—no prettier than what was unfolding in the spiritual eyes of the *Angelus Novus*. To be sure, it is not a well composed cosmos, a beautiful and harmonious Pandora Planet, but, as I said, a rather horrendous *kakosmos*. How could the Moderns have succeeded in assembling anything properly while *not looking at it*! It would be like playing the piano while turning one's back to the keyboard.... It is impossible to compose without being firmly attentive to the task at hand. But, horror of horrors, it does not have the same features as the archaic past from which they fled in terror for so long. For one good reason: from this horror you cannot flee! *It is coming at you.*[43] It's no use speaking of "epistemological breaks" anymore. Fleeing from the past while continuing to look at it will not do. Nor will critique be of any help. It is time to compose—in all the meanings of the word, including to compose with, that is to compromise, to care, to move slowly, with caution and precaution.[44] That's quite a new set of skills to learn: imagine that, innovating as never before but with precaution! Two great temptations here again, inherited from the time of the Great Flight: abandon all innovations; innovate as before without any precaution. The whole Modernist paraphernalia has to be remade bit by bit for the tasks that now lie ahead and no longer behind. Oedipus has met the Sphinx and she said: "Look ahead!" Was this not what she was actually alluding to with this odd simile: "Which creature in the morning goes on four legs, at midday on two, and in the evening upon three, and the more legs it has, the weaker it be?" Well, the Moderns of course, now knowing full well that they are blind and fumbling in the dark and that they need a white cane to slowly and cautiously feel the obstacles that lie ahead! The blind led by the blind are in great need of new captors and sensors—yes, new avatars.

What do the two manifestos have in common?

Why do I wish to reuse the oversized genre of the manifesto to explore this shift from future to prospect? Because in spite of the abyss of time, there is a tenuous relation between the Communist and the Compositionist Manifesto. At first sight, they seem utterly opposed. A belief in critique, in radical critique, a commitment to a fully idealized material world, a total confidence in the science of economics—economics, of all sciences!—a delight in the transformative power of negation, a trust in dialectics, a complete disregard for precaution, an abandon of liberty in politics behind a critique of liberalism, and, above all, an absolute trust in the inevitable thrust of progress. And yet, the two manifestos have something in common, namely the *search for the Common*. The thirst for the Common World is what there is of communism in compositionism, with this small but crucial difference that it has to be slowly composed instead of being taken for granted and *imposed* on all. Everything happens as if the human race were on the move again, expelled from one utopia, that of economics, and in search of another, that of ecology. Two different interpretations of one precious little root, *eikos*, the first being a dystopia and the second a promise that as yet no one knows how to fulfill. How can a livable and breathable "home" be built for those errant masses? That is the only question worth raising in this Compositionist Manifesto. If there is no durable room for us on Pandora, how will we find a sustainable home on Gaia?

Sciences Po, Paris

1
Bruno Latour, *Pandora's Hope: Essays on the Reality of Science Studies* (Cambridge, MA: Harvard Univ. Press, 1999).

2
James Lovelock, *The Revenge of Gaia: Earth's Climate in Crisis and the Fate of Humanity* (New York: Basic Books, 2006).

3
Funnily enough, Sigourney Weaver leads the charge, having to redo with the Navis what she did earlier with *Gorillas in the Mist*!...

4
Michel Tournier, *Friday, or, the Other Island*, trans. Norman Denny (Harmondsworth, UK: Penguin, 1984).

5
I realize that this is slightly contradictory and retains a modernist flavor by dividing time, once again, between before and now—but one has to accept to live with contradictions...

6
I thank Nina Wormbs for this microbial addition.

7
Scientists, politicians, engineers, lovers have a rich vocabulary to explore this difference, but this vocabulary is hidden in their practice and not easily summed up in the rules of method that are supposed to distinguish between true and false statements. The energy taken up by answering the question "is it constructed or is it true?" leaves no stamina to deploy the complex casuistic that answers, always locally and practically, the question "is it well or badly composed?" On this quandry, see Etienne Souriau, *Les différents modes d'existence : Suivi de "l'Oeuvre à faire"* (1943; Paris: Presses Univ. de France, 2009).

8
"Critique" is taken here in the meaning of the word introduced by Immanuel Kant, that is, a wholesale acceptation of the divide between human and nonhuman, not in the rather ubiquitous skill of having a critical mind.

9
Latour, "Why Has Critique Run Out of Steam? From Matters of Fact to Matters of Concern", *Critical Inquiry* 30, no. 2 (2004): 225–48.

10
Latour and Peter Weibel (eds.), *Iconoclash: Beyond the Image Wars in Science, Religion and Art* (Cambridge, MA: MIT Press, 2002).

11
Erle Ellis, "Stop Trying to Save the Planet", *Wired Science*, May 6, 2009.

12
This daring word was introduced in anthropology by Eduardo Viveiros de Castro. *Métaphysiques cannibales* (Paris: Presses Univ. de France, 2009).

13
Alfred North Whitehead, *Concept of Nature* (Cambridge: Cambridge Univ. Press,1920).

14
Latour, "Will Non-Humans be Saved? An Argument on Ecotheology", *Journal of the Royal Anthropological Institute* 5, no. 15 (2009): 459–75.

15
Latour, Politics of Nature: *How to Bring the Sciences into Democracy*, trans. Catherine Porter (Cambridge, MA: Harvard Univ. Press, 2004).

16
Most of the original documents may be found on *http://www.guardian.co.uk/environment/series/climate-wars-hacked-emails*

17
Michel Serres, *The Natural Contract*, trans. Elizabeth MacArthur and William Paulson (Ann Arbor: Univ. of Michigan Press, 1995) and "La non-invitée au sommet de Copenhague", *Libération*, December 9, 2009.

18
On this, see Walter Lippmann, *The Phantom Public* (1925; New Brunswick, NJ: Transactions Publishers, 1993) and my introduction to the French translation in Walter Lippmann, *Le Public fantôme*, trans. Laurence Decréau (Paris: Demopolis, 2008).

19
Steven Shapin and Simon Schaffer, *Leviathan and the Air-Pump: Hobbes, Boyle, and the Experimental Life* (Princeton, NJ: Princeton Univ. Press, 1985).

20
Stephen Toulmin, Cosmopolis: *The Hidden Agenda of Modernity* (Chicago: Univ. of Chicago Press, 1990).

21
An implementation, we should never forget, that has always been disputed since it is impossible to be really modern—except in dreams or nightmares.

22
I am alluding here to Lorraine Daston and Katharine Park, *Wonders and the Order of Nature, 1150–1750* (Cambridge, MA: Zone Books, 1999).

23
This is what makes the controversy over the very existence of an epistemological break between the Renaissance and the so-called Classic Age so interesting. On this, see Horst Bredekamp, *The Lure of Antiquity and the Cult of the Machine: The Kunstkammer and the Evolution of Nature, Art, and Technology*, trans. Allison Brown (Princeton, NJ: M. Wiener Publishers, 1995), for a clear opposition to Foucault's rendering of the distinction.

24
Alexandre Koyré, *From the Closed World to the Infinite Universe* (Baltimore: Johns Hopkins Univ. Press, 1957).

25
A question which humanists and literary studies are actually better equipped than most social sciences to deal with, thanks to their attention to the complex semiosis of human and nonhuman fictional characters, as can be seen in the writing of Richard Powers (see for instance, one of his latest novels, *The Echo Maker* [New York: Farrar, Strauss and Giroux, 2006]) as well as in the renewal of literary theory, for instance Rita Felski, *Uses of Literature* (Oxford: Blackwell Publishers, 2008). The redistribution of agencies is the right purview of literature studies, see Françoise Bastide, *Una notte con Saturno. Scritti semiotici sul discorso scientifico*, trans. Roberto Pellerey (Rome: Meltemi, 2001).

26
From James Lovelock, *Gaia: A New Look at Life on Earth* (Oxford: Oxford Univ. Press, 1979) to *The Vanishing Face of Gaia* (New York: Basic Books, 2009). On Lovelock's move from marginality to centrality, see the biography by John Gribbin and Mary Gribbin. *James Lovelock: In Search of Gaia* (Princeton, NJ: Princeton Univ. Press, 2009).

27
Which means that in practice the necessity of establishing chains of reference for knowing a state of affairs is confused with the ways in which this state of affairs maintains itself and sustains its existence. On this confusion between modes of existence, see my "A Textbook Case Revisited: Knowledge as a Mode of Existence," in Edward Hackett et al., *The Handbook of Science and Technology Studies*, 3rd ed. (Cambridge, MA: MIT Press, 2007), 83–111.

28
Latour, "Irreductions", in *The Pasteurization of France* (Cambridge, MA: Harvard Univ. Press, 1988).

29
In his masterpiece, the most important book of anthropology to appear in French since Levi-Strauss's enterprise, Philippe Descola in *Par-delà nature et culture* (Paris: Gallimard, 2005) distinguishes four essentially different ways of gathering collectives: totemism and analogism on the one hand, and animism and naturalism on the other.

30
Alfred North Whitehead, *Process and Reality: An Essay in Cosmology* (1929; New York: Free Press, 1978).

31
Evelyn Fox Keller, *The Century of the Gene* (Cambridge, MA: Harvard Univ. Press, 2000).

32
Hans-Jörg Rheinberger, *Toward a History of Epistemic Things: Synthetizing Proteins in the Test Tube* (Stanford, CA: Stanford Univ. Press, 1997).

33
Jean-Jacques Kupiec and Pierre Sonigo, *Ni Dieu ni gène* (Paris: Seuil, 2000).

34
The notion of *eikos* is being deeply renewed by the new attention to "envelopes" and "spheres" in the vast enterprise of Peter Sloterdijk. Unfortunately, of his three-tome work on "spherology", only *Terror from the Air*, trans. Amy Patton and Steve Corcoran (Los Angeles: Semiotext(e), 2009) is available in English. The best introduction to his thought is to be found in Peter Sloterdijk, *Neither Sun Nor Death: A Dialog with Hans-Jürgen Heinrichs*, trans. Steve Corcoran (Los Angeles: Semiotext(e), 2010).

35
This has nothing to do with the red-herring of "hylozoism" (David Skrbina, *Panpsychism in the West* [Cambridge, MA: MIT Press, 2007]) because the matter invented by modernism is not proper to any sort of life…

36
Noortje Marres, *No Issue, No Public: Democratic Deficits after the Displacement of Politics* (PhD Diss., Amsterdam, 2005).

37
For what is now fifteen years, with the help of many colleagues, I have devised methods to map out scientific and technical controversies and explore this new navigation through controversial datascapes. For a review of methods and case studies see *http://www.mappingcontroversies.net/*

38
Translated by Dennis Redmond (creative commons license) *http://www.marxists.org/reference/archive/benjamin/1940/history.htm*

39
An odd notion to be sure, but as the anthropological inquiry I have pursued for so long shows time and time again: everything is odd in modernism.

40
There is good reason to define this character as a He rather than a She, as so much feminist literature has shown, from Carolyn Merchant's early work, *The Death of Nature: Women, Ecology and the Scientific Revolution* (London: Wildwood House, 1980) all the way to Donna J. Haraway, *When Species Meet* (Minneapolis: Minnesota Univ. Press, 2007), a compositionist book if ever there was one.

41
In Toulmin's rendition, it is clearly the religious wars that they were fleeing in terror and that justified the strange counter-revolution that is wrongly called by him the scientific revolution. But four centuries later, the much more benign "science wars" show the same flight from the horrors of irrationality.

42
No more than matters of facts and matters of concern, critique and composition, or, to allude to another transformation I have not commented on here, society and collective. On this last see *Reassembling the Social: An Introduction to Actor-Network Theory* (Oxford: Oxford Univ. Press, 2005).

43
Isabelle Stengers, *Au temps des catastrophes: Résister à la barbarie qui vient* (Paris: Les Empêcheurs, 2009).

44
"Precaution" has become a legal term of great interest in European affairs, analogous to the word "risk", as evidenced by the telltale book of Ulrich Beck, *Risk Society: Towards a New Modernity* (London: Sage, 1992).

Page 41

16 Images of the Week

They were asked for during a course. Images that would spark an interest, not selected with a first evidence of their belonging. Whether to an artistic or scientific reality, at a second glance they reveal further relations.

Page 42

Radiation Warning Symbol

Page 43

Council flats

Page 44

Where's Alice?

Page 45

The Ash Yggdrasil

Page 46

Caption 1963

Page 47

A landscape as line

ausgenommen
Dienstfahrzeuge
der Bundespolizei
·Anfang·
Ende

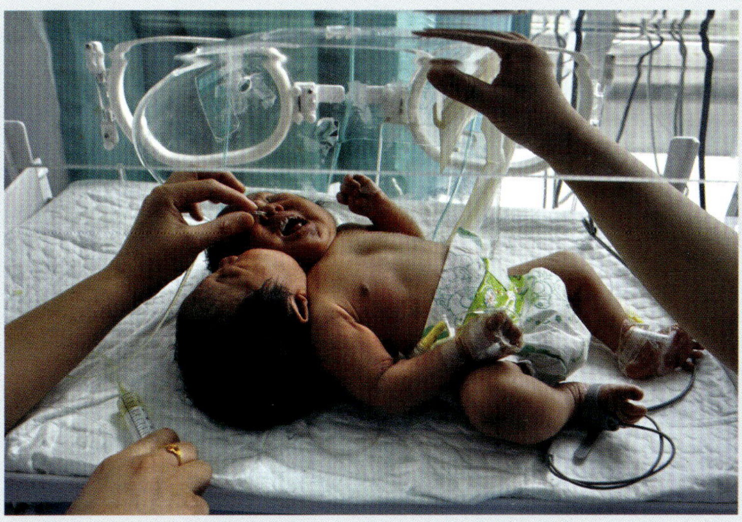

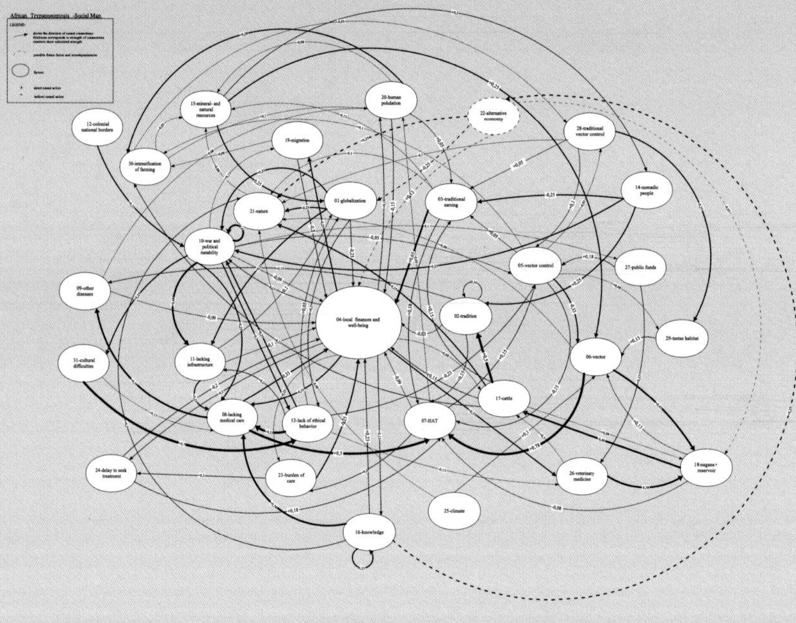

Page 50

Fuzzy cognitive map showing the interdependencies between parasites and African culture using the example of sleeping sickness and nagana

Page 51

German Panther

POLIERARTIKEL

Page 54

The Chimera

Page 55

The natural and the historic – a mixed reality

Page 56

Relativity

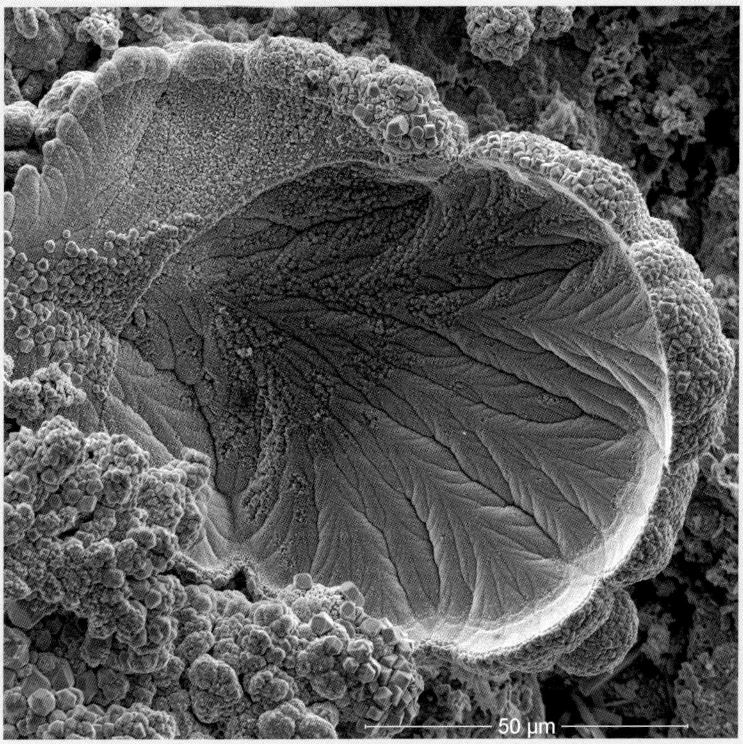

Page 57

Transformer (12.4 V) with coarse paper structure

Page 42 Sarah Duit

Radiation Warning Symbol

At the time, this image was very present in the media because of the catastrophe in Fukushima, so I couldn't avoid it. I realised how much symbolism and emotion this image transports. With a middle European cultural and historic background, it tells so much about danger, fear, accidents, and malformations... although the pictogram itself is not very explicit.

This sign loses its meaning when taken out of the context of our current science-driven environment and thinking. It represents a technology and, in conjunction with (popular) scientific reports, generates a picture in the mind of the public. Therefore, it plays an essential role in creating a reality with nuclear plants, atomic waste, and radiation hazard.

Page 43 Michaela Grass

Council flats, 2011

Small idyll: to live in council flats is different. A bit different than elsewhere. Good and bad. Away from the prejudice of those, who know this type of living only from television. Especially here, life is "not anonymous". A very little idyll, or not? We should say, not always idyllic.

Page 44 Rudolf Friemel

Where's Alice?, 2011

The photo shows, in a way, the environment and approach artistic researchers are into – the human world consists of nested systems, which sometimes lack connections between aspects. Imagine a road sign showing the way to a location. It gives you a starting or re-starting point to reach a certain destination. When travelling on, there is a distance between the previous road sign and the next one. This gap is filled out with either knowledge or abstraction. Creativity bridges the absence to enable a continuous system. I chose this image because of its depiction of a common myth, which is not limited to the environment shown in the photograph. Everything we do leaves something behind for others to analyse or work with. Every approach is individual, and so is that which people do when they perceive coherencies.

Page 45 Anna Fríða Jónsdóttir

The Ash Yggdrasil, Friedrich Wilhelm Heine, in: Wilhelm Wägner, Asgard and the Gods (London: Swan Sonnenschein, Le Bas & Lowrey, 1886), 27.

According to Jung, the God archetype represents our need to comprehend the universe, to give a meaning to all that happens, to see it all as having some purpose and direction. This need still exists within the modern man, but it seems that for the average Western person this need has shifted from religion to science. We crave to understand, but some things are simply not within our reach to see or fully comprehend. Sometimes, it simply comes down to faith and expectations, something completely irrational and unexplainable. These cases are what interest me. I crave to understand why some things are the way they are, but no one really knows why.

We just accept the fact that we don't understand. Explanations of these phenomena can be found in philosophy, mythology, and religion. Science touches on these topics and more than often gets stuck – but sometimes an explanation is found, and therein lies the magic. My aim is to look into these topics and try to understand what it is that we humans generally believe.

Page 46 Pepa Bugueiro Domingo

Dr. Strangelove, Stanley Kubrick, 1963

"On a fine November day in 1945, late in the afternoon, I was landed on an airstrip in Southern Japan. [...] The moment of recognition when I realised that I was already in Nagasaki is present to me as I write, as vividly as when I lived it. I see the warm night and the meaningless shapes; I can even remember the tune that was coming from the ship. It was a dance tune which had been popular in 1945, and it was called Is You Is Or Is You Ain't Ma Baby? [...] And civilization asks of both ruins [...]." Jacob Bronowski, *Science and Human Values* (London: Hutchinson 1961), 13–15.

Page 47 Richard Schwarz

A landscape as line, Pencil on translucent paper, 2011

Drawing a line draws attention to things that we try to understand. A line is – next to a point – the most radical form of abstraction, which erases a lot of information through representing. But in this reduction also answers are found. The line is a directory that leads us to new ideas, possible solutions, and ways of thinking.

Page 48 Iulian Moise

Untitled, 2011

The presence of authority – it's around us? Between us? Over us? Beneath us? Where, when, how does it begin? Where, when, how, why does it end?

Page 49 Anna Fáter

In this photo taken Monday, May 9, 2011, medical workers attend to conjoined twin babies with a single body and two heads born on May 5 in a hospital in Suining city in southwestern China's Sichuan province. The local Huaxi Metropolis Daily says the twins weighed nine pounds (4 kg) and measured 20 inches (51 centimeters) and have two spines, two esophaguses and shared other organs. Doctors were quoted as saying it would be nearly impossible to separate them.

Looking at the image, I think of humanity and that we should take care for our planet and think more about the consequences of our actions. We should act with more care, maybe. I myself try to act with more attention, to respond and deal with my surroundings.

Page 50 Michael Bachhofer

Fuzzy cognitive map showing the interdependencies between parasites and African culture using the example of sleeping sickness and nagana, 2008

This fuzzy cognitive map was my first project with fuzzy cognitive mapping (FCM). Research on parasites, especially Glossinidae and Trypanosomatidae, played a big role during many years of my life. I like FCMs because they enable us to display complex relations in a clear and formal way. It is easy to develop mathematical models out of the graphical representation.

Page 51 Alin Cîrstea

German Panther, Hans Hemmert, balloon/air/glue, 960 x 370 x 300cm, 2007

Honestly, I do not know for what reasons I chose this image. I figure I liked the contrast of its content. A tank made out of balloons. Inoffensive destruction. Colourful camouflage. Fading durability. The man staring at it in wonder, not sure how to react. Child and oversized toy? Don't know. What I do remember about this image is that, the first time I saw it, I smiled. Maybe that's the reason.

Page 52 David Palme

Because of a demonstration against the ball of the "Wiener Korporationsring" (WKR) the police widely blocked the area around Westbahnstraße in Vienna on January 28, 2011.

A functional patch on a police uniform becomes a statement of power – an occurence that I do not take for granted.

Page 53 Ashley Holwell

Untitled, 2011

Within ourselves and the universe, there is a melange of diverse indispensable elements in perpetual autopoiesis at all scales. And we have consciousness, at a range of scales. A reconciliation of this ill-dealt-with paradox is of particular interest to me.

Page 54 Michal Marencik

The Chimera, Mutated photography, 2008

The image shows a seemingly average, standard human, which bears no racial signification but displays some form of mythical content hidden in its angelic wings. The mythical Chimera – the sister of Kerberos, Orthus, Sphinx, and Hydra – was a combination of a lion, a goat, and a dragon. This chimera is more human but could be perceived both as an animal or the result of bioengineering approaches to change human genetic information. The first inspiration to create this image was the thought of a crowd – the human mass losing its concrete shapes and forms. Imperfection morphed and compressed into a figure that could be read as a religious or mythical creature that significantly resembles a human.

Page 55 Sabina Teichert

The natural and the historic – a mixed reality, 2010

At the beginning of the first semester, I started to write down all my questions in a notebook. I chose this image because it is the last one glued into my "question book", and I am generally unable to answer its questions. The not-answering and not-knowing is painful. When I look at the chewed off bones and the morbid image I took at the Museum of Natural History, I get a feeling of *weltschmerz*. For the moment, I cannot elaborate further on this. Life and death. In-between an immense spectrum of what happens on Earth, how matters are dealt with. On whose behalf, "who is speaking for whom", and "who is doing research for whom"?

Page 56 Manuel Stark

Relativity, M.C. Escher, Lithograph, 1953

Page 57 Leon Ploszczanski

Transformer (12.4 V) with coarse paper structure, Scanning electron microscopy image, 2011

This picture is fascinating as it is hard to find an image of these delicate structures in such clarity. Most of the time, the bubbles are overgrown with other copper crystals and are therefore hidden. I was just lucky to find this one.

16 Images of the Week

Twice a Month
guest speakers are invited to lecture at the Art & Science studio

00:00:00.00

A central part of a scientific paper is its "Materials and Methods" section that helps colleagues to understand and reproduce a given experimental set-up. It is this closer look that may decide upon the (mis)fortune or further development of the finding. In the Jour Fixe we provide a forum for discussion that aims to approach the practice of artistic and scientific methods. It is about the questions of traceability, precision and rigour, about the role of (lucky) chance, contingencies and accidents, about processes and plans, sketches and (art)works. Is there a necessity to use a "method"? What is a method actually "doing" – not merely in its context but also in a societal sense? Is a method a constraint that should be avoided? The guests report on their work and their approaches to engage with interdisciplinary boundaries, artistic positions, and sociocultural or economic strategies. In the best case, the audience experiences how things, processes, concepts, or matters of concern that may affect us are generated, negotiated, or constructed.

Friday, 21 January 2011

Thomas Bugnyar – Raven Politics: Understanding and Use of Social Relationships

Thomas Bugnyar is a professor for cognitive ethology and part of the newly founded Department of Cognitive Biology at the University of Vienna. His research focuses on social behaviour and complex cognition in non-human animals, ranging from social learning, perspective taking, and "theory of mind" to forms of cooperation and conflict management. He was invited as a Jour Fixe guest to the Art & Science department. The following questions and answers came up in the discussion after the lecture.

00:55:49.22

Q: How do you interpret the social behaviour of the ravens when they are subdominants or dominants? How does this influence the research? Do you have preferences?

00:56:38.05

Thomas Bugnyar: In the original tests, I had this as one of the parameters. So each raven was basically confronted one time with subordinates, another time with dominant competitors. And depending on the situation you may find differences. For instance, a high-ranking bird tested with a subordinate as potential pilferer doesn't care about what the other one has or hasn't seen. He could get the food anyway, if necessary by using force. However, for a subordinate, things are different: he needs to be quicker to the cache than the competitor when this one has also seen the caching (because if the cache is still intact when the dominant arrives, he will get the food for sure); he can delay pilfering and wait for the competitor to leave the area, albeit only if this one didn't see the cache being made before. So there are certainly effects of dominance. In fact, pilfering other's caches is the most effective strategy for subordinates. Dominants can also go for scrounging or direct kleptoparasitism, i.e. "You have something I want. Give it to me, otherwise I'll take it by force." They do well in direct competition for food, following the rule of thumb "those with superior power get the resources"; this is a general principal you can find in several social animals. The interesting switch in ravens is when it comes to competition about hidden food: there, having physical power doesn't matter anymore. Because if birds could control their intentions and wait until potential competitors are out of sight, then also subordinates can steal caches. And so the game switches from being physical to being mental.

01:07:35.38

Q: When is there a difference made between animals being more dominant based on size and cognitive contributes?

01:07:35.60

TB: Difficult to say, but probably not too often. In many species of primates, the outcome of competition is mainly based on physical strength; in some, however, you hardly find good correlations or very weak correlations with physical strength. What is going on with the latter species is that individuals help each other in conflicts. So they basically are trying to make up for physical power by playing tactically. For instance, in conflicts they may think, "Is this individual stronger than me? Who do I need to help me overpower him? And how do I get the other one to help me?" And this is what is going on with the ravens, too; maybe not in exactly the same way as in primates, but the general line is the same. Hence, we can find the development of cognitive strategies, departing from mere domination via physical power to manipulating others by using the brain, in at least some mammals and some birds.

01:08:47.04

Q: Is there any evidence that kinship plays a role?

01:08:57.36

TB: Not in caching. When it comes to caching, friendship is over and even kinship is over. This stands in contrast to providing help in conflicts or cooperation in general. Here, social relationships – in particular affiliate relationships like friendship, kinship, and partnership – do play quite a role. This is actually the topic of my current programme "Raven Politics", where I try to find out what the birds know about their social relationships and how flexibly they use this knowledge. One argument could be: It's all about kinship. This is certainly not the case. For instance, if there are three siblings, let's say three brothers, then it is likely that two of them will become very close, forming a strong alliance against all others; the third one is left out, and he has to look for a "friend" somewhere else. Hence, it seems to be important for ravens to have one particular ally that they can really rely on. Indeed, they work very hard on those "friendships", notably by providing grooming, sharing food, etc. What they do when the other one defects is very cool, too – they seem to get really upset, harassing non-reliable individuals as if they want to make sure: "No, you won't do that again!"

01:10:08.44

Q: Have you made studies about the perception of the ravens, what they can see?

01:10:17.23

TB: We are currently investigating this because we have started to use computers and videos quite intensively. And for these things it is very necessary to understand what they really see. We know that birds, in general, see very well, much better than us. They also have more than three colour receptors, at least one more than humans; notably, they can also see UV. Hence, I checked for possible UV reflections on the feathers as I thought that this might be a problem when we are testing with videos. Obviously, when they have UV sensitivity and they reflect UV, they cannot see the appropriate images/colours on our monitors because those are made for our vision and not for theirs. So we measured the UV reflections of the feathers. To our surprise, it turned out that there is hardly any on the feathers, just on the beak and the feet. So for a raven, they have something colourful on the beak and the feet, everything else is as black as it is for us.

01:13:30.65

Q: So you can make tests with them with screens?

01:13:37.11

TB: We did a pilot so far. We showed them videos of ravens that they didn't know and of other birds, namely a goose – trying to control for effects of size (it could be that they are interested in big things) – and a crow, a close relative, that looks very similar to ravens. And it turned out that they have a strong preference to watch ravens, so they can perfectly discriminate between the species. And they also have preferences to watch the opposite sex of ravens, so the males watch the females more and the females the males. This was striking to me because there was no sound and hardly any movement. The clips were actually very boring. All you could see was a raven sitting there. And the males got really happy seeing a female and vice versa. Thus, they could definitely get the species and sex information out of the video. In the near future, I'd like to use videos to test what they know about relationships, not only about their relations to others (like "this is my friend", "this is a dominant", etc.), but also about the relations amongst other individuals (like "this is the friend of X", "this is the offspring of Y"). The latter is called third-party understanding; it is cognitively demanding and has been assumed to be unique to primates.

01:16:49.09

Q: How is the human observer influencing the observation?

01:17:00.74

TB: I always remember in the States, where I worked with ravens a lot, that I had experimental parts and observation parts. The ravens really liked the experimental parts, but in the observation parts I was boring to them. When I switched from the observation part to the experimental part they became very aroused and happy. They started to become happy even when I just started to think that it was time to switch to the experiment and end the observation. So then I was playing around with what cues they use to know that I was going to switch. When I was speaking in the voice recorder, I observed that a short pause and a little smile sufficed. This was enough that they would know that now the really interesting thing starts. It was also the other way around, when the experiment was over I always raised my hands to signal "stop". Then they turned around and did something else. There is a lot of interaction going on. This is the interesting thing with ravens: they are quick learners and very apt in picking up human-given cues – which makes them perfect "students" in our cognitive experiments.

Excerpt of discussion after the lecture "Raven Politics: Understanding and Use of Social Relationships" on Friday, 21 January 2011

Friday, 8 April 2011

Valérie Pihet – Experiments on Arts and Politics

Valérie Pihet is the executive director of the Master of Experiments on Arts and Politics programme at Sciences Po in Paris. She has collaborated with Bruno Latour since 2002, who recently became vice-president of research at Sciences Po. The new master programme is defined by experimentation and inquiry steeped in pragmatic mechanisms that combine the practices of arts and social sciences. On the basis of practical issues mooted by commission or by request, the task is to investigate the creation of a problematised space that is public, shared, and participative, yet still the locus of necessarily controversial issues. In her lecture, Valérie Pihet described experiences made within the first year of the programme and responded to questions put forward.

02:56:29.34

Q: The floor is open.

02:56:50.84

Valérie Pihet: Can I add something? People often wonder, "What is art in that?" talking about inquiry, social sciences, and politics. We don't believe that the artists are the only ones who are sensitive and that the social scientists are the ones who are supposedly "objective". It would mean getting rid of years of research on what sciences (science studies) are and simplifying the definition of arts.

02:57:55.04

Q: Is the project more or less about

solving problems together? You said that you bring different people together and then you find an innovative solution. Does that mean that it is all about innovation, if you bring their ideas and tools together?

02:58:42.31

VP: It is not about solving problems rather more about finding an accurate representation for an issue. The question of representation has to be thought again, facing the increasing complexity of our planet. We have to be careful with the word "innovation". I'm not sure we invent anything new, but we should try to work with different tools and skills from various fields of research. Bruno Latour likes to talk about "composition". What is nice about the word composition is that it is related to artistic practices, but also to care, respect, negotiation, and compromise. It is a beautiful word. By experimenting with composition and confronting methods, artists and scientists can improve their own research/fields, while dealing with common concerns of our society.

In the exhibition *Making Things Public*, I was surprised that there was a lot of criticism about the show. It was again always the same discussions about scientists instrumentalising artists, and the opposite. And it was also about: "What is that object? Is it an art piece? Or a scientific piece? Or what is it?" These are not the right questions. I think the show was indeed disputable – but not in that way. For me, it was about looking for what the "object" – whatever it is, artistic or not – is telling us. The Master of Experiments on Arts and Politics programme is more interesting because it is directly connected to people who face problems in their activities. With the exhibition we failed a little bit, maybe because the show is already a closed form. Some pieces didn't work.

03:03:33.40

Q: What do you mean "didn't work"?

03:03:36.32

VP: For example, some pieces were quite illustrative and did not tell anything new about the concerns. I think we can discuss that but not say: "Oh, that is not an art piece", or "Oh, is it a scientific piece?" It is very difficult and demanding to combine content and form. It can easily fail, but it is still crucial to experiment with it because it tells a lot about the issues, about the artist, about the scientist. The critique wasn't constructive. And this is what Bruno [Latour] means with "overcome the critical". It doesn't mean that you can't say anything, but for him postmodernism is like critique of critique. And now, what do we do with that? So we must go further and overcome this.

03:13:12.12

Q: You spoke about the inability of politics to develop accurate means, maybe a language, on one hand, and then you made a very interesting and important point about not practising whatever problem you come up with at the school, rather taking it to the real world. But then, in the outcome, you combine arts and sciences or arts and politics, and you develop something even more abstract, even more complex. You develop another language by mixing up two disciplines.

03:14:24.80

VP: You mean we put more complexity within the complexity? I think the complexity can't be solved by separating disciplines; we can see it today very well, don't you think? At some point, we have to confront what we know about a concern in different fields and see what else we learn. It does not mean we have to mix the disciplines, make them disappear or lose their particularities, rather we have to enable disciplines to learn from each other.

03:14:40.20

Q: I'm just wondering whether this can be an outcome or whether it is a contradiction between the main goals. A lot of the time, you experience that the projects make a lot of sense to the people who did them, and also to a very small group of people who have the intellectual background to read that type of media. But for a lot of other people it is meaningless because they don't have an adequate access point. If I were to write a new curriculum for an art and science programme, I wonder if that wouldn't be the key feature of the programme itself – to question the gap between the accessibility of the work and the actual production of the work.

03:15:33.72

VP: That is a very interesting question. You mean what we will do with the results? How will they be used or become visible – or not – for other people, the commissioners, and so on?

03:16:03.54

Q: I mean there is a general danger in this kind of studies that they become a self-fulfilling prophecy and maybe self-fulfilling entertainment. You work for a while, get some funds, you secure your life, and then afterwards, you put it somewhere and that is it. And it is not going further.

03:16:33.75

VP: That's exactly what we want to test with our programme. That's why the commissioners (people who deal with problems, like people not paying) are fully involved in the project. We are all responsible before each other. It is a very delicate process of negotiation and mediation. The other big question raised by the school is how to make an experiment visible, readable for many people, without losing the necessary specificity of the case. Each case is very specific, but from each one you can learn something. It is very difficult to translate experiments, but that is the challenge. Maybe, sometimes, we need to accept that it will work in one place and time and try to be optimistic about people who will take benefit of the experiment and pursue it in other places and times. We are aware of the danger, but we want to create a space in which we can confront these questions, where the answers are not given.

03:17:04.66

Q: I would like to add another dimension to that question. If I follow the pragmatist connotation of John Dewey and others, concerning what the public is, and start a project like this, it is a built-in problem to follow the logic of this issue and its public who can read this. And it is not readable for the others, so it disappears again. The challenge is not to find a universal question for an artwork, which can hold anywhere.

03:17:25.75

VP: You are right. According to John Dewey, "the public" doesn't exist. You as an individual are a part of a lot of different publics. In your work, in your life, you are involved in different kinds of activities, and for each activity, you are involved in different publics. And as soon as one problem or issue is solved, the public disappears because there is no issue anymore. We want to experiment with the thinking of John Dewey; we want to try it out concretely, but it can fail.

03:18:16.10

Q: One more thing, there is the problem people in scientific surroundings have: In order to get funds from the government or other organisations, there is a lot of paperwork and precise definition of what you will do beforehand. And because you have these funds, these limitations, what you do, in the end, is prove what you put in your very first concept. At Sciences Po, is there a concept of being more open, to embrace making mistakes?

03:19:32.52

VP: It is unfortunately true. It is always as if we have answers before asking the question. It is more difficult to get results within the programme because of that, because the trajectory for scientists is more difficult than for artists. We have more artists because they are more accustomed to work with projects. They can deal with our programme as it is not a full-time programme; they can do other activities and then come to us. For a researcher, it is more difficult because the trajectory is more defined and there aren't so many choices. A lot of researchers are unhappy with this. A lot of them would like to do our programme, but they can't as you can't miss one year in their trajectory. I'm not sure if we will start the revolution at Sciences Po, but we try to open a door.

03:22:15.34

Q: Your programme tries to link the practice with the real world in these projects. I'm interested to see and hear about how students tackle this kind of uncertainty they experience in the different projects and find their own voice. You have this commissioner structure… but then, how do they tackle the whole situation of being in the midst of this uncertainty of the project, the mess of the world around, the team? There is this shift to represent somebody else's issue or to do a service, but how does one find an own voice while being in this kind of situation?

03:25:35.35

VP: We are in the middle of that, so it is difficult to have distance. From a human point of view, I think it is a very hard experiment. For some of them, it is very difficult because they become fragile. Some are still proving something. Every week, the students have to come to the school; they work in groups on projects, and then we discuss all projects together. And the atmosphere there is surprisingly good. They disagree, sometimes there are fights, some tensions, but generally they succeed. They know they are there for that, and they know it is the only rule of the school – to play the game. It is very intense and very messy.

03:27:34.72

Q: It is great in this kind of learning situation to have the experience of being thrown in a real world situation, since you can't be in the role of the artist or the sociologist anymore. It is then more about dealing with shifting the roles and being instrumentalised.

03:28:01.68

VP: Again, I don't think we shift the roles, and I don't think it is about instrumentalising… It is more about negotiation, mediation, and translation. Actually, I think one must hang on to their role.

03:34:29.46

Q: John Dewey talks about finding one's own language, which I understood with Bruno Latour as a kind of translation, when one finds their own way of doing. Coming from the arts, my problem is to reject having an object as a representation more often. What to do with that? I cannot permanently redo and redo. First of all, I'm used to making a decision because the piece has to be finished. And secondly, I cannot imagine an alternative to having an object as a representation.

03:35:50.49

VP: About the language, we are more interested in what can be a common language, which allows us to learn about an issue, and not an individual language. But it doesn't mean you have to compromise personality. That is the difficulty in the project – to keep the heterogeneity while doing something else. Maybe it is a misunderstanding if I talk about the form and the object because it doesn't necessarily have to be an object. It can be an action. A lot of artists do actions. It is not necessarily an object, that is for sure. I will give you an example: During the Saint Denis project, dealing with a facility for drug users, we spent one day with Isabelle Stengers, and she said something very interesting and helpful. We were talking about this visibility question, like you said: "What is the form?" And she proposed to us, instead of interviewing the inhabitants and the neighbourhood, it could be about telling them that they did something good – because, in reality, not one of the neighbours attacked the association in Saint Denis. Very often, the inhabitants sue the association because they don't want drug users in their streets. So you could just tell the people that what they are doing is great and that they can be proud of that. It is another way of formulating the question of visibility. It is not a performance, it is not a form, it is not a photograph, it is not an object, but it is something.

Excerpt of discussion after the lecture "Experiments on Arts and Politics" on Friday, 8 April 2011

Thursday, 26 May 2011

Nikolaus Gansterer – Figures of Research or Harvesting the Tree of Knowledge

Nikolaus Gansterer studied transmedia art at the University of Applied Arts in Vienna. He co-founded the Institute for Transacoustic Research and The Vegetable Orchestra. In his visual work he focuses on mapping processes emerging out of cultural and scientific networks, unfolding their immanent structures of interconnectedness. Nikolaus Gansterer was a guest at the Jour Fixe on 25 November 2010 and gave a talk on "Figures of Research or Harvesting the Tree of Knowledge". As the recording of his talk was broken, we met him on 26 May 2011 with some questions about his ongoing work.

00:00:46.36

Q: As the main focus of your work lies in the exploration of drawing as a time-based process, in how far do you use drawing as a method?

00:00:50.81

Nikolaus Gansterer: Drawing, for me, is a method of perception, but it also has to do with the translation of thought processes. Accordingly, my recent application to the Program for Arts-based Research (PEEK), which is funded by the Austrian Science Fund (FWF), should help to further elaborate this interest. My intention is to investigate the relationship between thinking and drawing. Surprisingly, I found that the topic has not been investigated very well to date. There are some works in design and in architecture that deal with the production of drafts. It is impossible to explain a complex building – like a house, for instance – only through talking. The drawing functions as a helpful instrument to narrow down the creative essentials in such elaborate projects.

00:02:04.18

Q: Do you also understand the drawing as an archive, as a recording device?

00:02:40.45

NG: In my experience, I learned that it is easier to communicate an idea by using a pencil. Using the pencil also helps to bring the idea more and more into shape. The method of scribbling, doodling, or making a short note pinpoints a thought and establishes a diagrammatic relation to the white paper and the concept. From this point of view, representing a reality is less important. Drawing is a good way to get in contact with the so called subconscious and the undercurrent influences of a thought. By starting with a preliminary series of sketches, often a more matured idea for a work will appear. Over the entire process the drawing might change a lot in its functionality. Ultimately, the drawing could actually represent the initial idea in the resulting installation but in a different way than in the first introspection, where the drawing depicted something not yet existent. I am highly interested in all these developments.

00:04:58.17

Q: In addition to simply making drawings, you also transform drawings with different types of media. For instance, you also include the sound of the drawing in your performances. Is the aim, thereby, to create transmedia art works and to deviate from the traditional notion of the drawing?

00:05:18.28

NG: Drawing is like a film that includes different phases. The finished drawing shows a frozen period of time. If you record the process with video and look at it afterwards, you can get a vague idea of how the brain functions. You don't see the temporal lines in the finished drawing. This interests me very much in the live-drawings, where the drawing becomes a performative element, like choreography on paper. The paper is like the stage of a theatre where the pencil and the drawing hand are the protagonists. Together, they leave traces that can be interpreted by an audience.

00:10:27.43

Q: Do you rehearse for your performances?

00:10:51.40

NG: For *De-Stilling Life*, a work I did in collaboration with the Dutch artist Wietske Maas in the Kunsthistorisches Museum in Vienna, we often sat down together to develop mental maps and discuss them. The preparations were necessary to find a more systematic approach to all the various references. By doing these studies we could determine where a more, let's say, psychological view should be applied and where it is more a geopolitical reference. I do rehearse – or better, I "practise".

00:14:40.96

Q: In how far are collaborations significant in your work?

00:15:05.58

NG: For me, it is important that there is a separate space only for my own work, where I'm the decision maker. But I also like to work in groups. In groups you can pursue ideas you couldn't otherwise realise. Nevertheless, collaborative projects often might take much longer. As I have been working with sound for a long time, I have experienced in music that it is very normal to work in groups; whereas in the fine arts, an ego-type artist is promoted. Sometimes, I feel more like a jazz musician in a fine arts environment. I use my own tools, but I don't refrain from sharing my work.

00:22:42.96

Q: Do you have a long-term project, a long-term research question that you are pursuing?

00:22:46.37

NG: My interest is in how things relate to each other and how these relations can be retraced and depicted. It has less to do with abstraction; it is more about explaining complexities through an equally complex system and doing this in the form of downscaled models that make the arrangements apprehensible. Every research has to have a focus, but I still want to keep multiple dimensions in play.

Above all, I'm very fascinated with diagrams because they are able to show the relations between things and not just the objects themselves. In the exploration of in between spaces it is possible to gain information about the objects, too. One can draw two objects, but one can also draw the intermediate space and thereby also involve the objects as well. It works like a tilt picture: you don't look at the things rather right through them; they still exist, but you shift your focus to the in-between space. You see the same image, but you process it differently. The diagram is about scaling the significant points to a certain distance and depicting the relations. The concept as well as the aesthetic of the diagram is particularly interesting.

A term I took out of the scientific context to describe my work is the "figure". I understand my work as figures, which might relate to a number, a result, or a diagram. The term "figure" also refers to something in movement, something that keeps on changing and evolving. My pieces are like partial results; they can be disassembled and newly constructed into a different set of pieces by still being in a mode of communication with each other.

<u>Excerpt of an interview on Thursday, 26 May 2011</u>

Wednesday, 16 June 2010

Victoria Vesna – Art|Science Collaborations: Being in Between

Victoria Vesna is a media artist and professor at the UCLA Department of Design | Media Arts and director of the Art|Sci Center at the School of the Arts and the California Nanosystems Institute (CNSI). On Wednesday, 16 June 2010, she was invited to present her work by the Science Visualization department at the University of Applied Arts Vienna. In her talk she recounted how her collaborations with scientists started, often out of friendships. As a spokesperson of a "Third Culture" she also gave insight on how to communicate science as an artist.

00:38:24.99

Victoria Vesna: Working in the academic context, at one point I realised that I was just repeating the status quo by following the existing structures. So I decided that if I am in the educational sector, I would make a commitment to innovation and follow the footsteps of inspiring people like the composer Schönberg, who was at UCLA in the 40s. He was fabulous in his music but also made huge innovative strides in the education of musicians in particular. I never really felt a separation between my work and the academic space, which I thought was the case for a lot of my colleagues in the arts. The campus became my playspace and my studio – I would not simply be there, teach, and then leave. You never stop. You only work in different environments. And I have been doing this with very conscious intent.

Soon after 9/11, I organised the symposium "From Networks to Nanosystems". I invited Jim Gimzewski to give a talk because I wanted to have an actual nanoscientist – not only a bunch of artists and theoreticians – discussing nanoscience. We have been collaborating ever since.

These are literally his words: "One nanometre across we are looking at electron probabilities and waves here. It's mainly empty space." There is nothing physical about this. In fact, it is metaphysical and poetic, and this is one of the main points I find so inspiring about working in nanospace.

Connected to that, I wanted to do something with the buckyball [*showing the molecular abacus of Jim Gimzewski*]. What you see here is the molecular abacus Jim created. It is the smallest abacus on the planet, and it was in the *Guinness Book of World Records* – he would tell you this proudly.

These are the buckyballs made in his lab [*showing buckyball models*]. And when I asked him if they had some models to work from, they showed me these very plastic looking visualisations and models. I thought, "Do you really believe that molecules look like shiny plastic?" Not to mention that nothing is ever as static as it is presented. So I started working on it. Instead of going into a molecular scale, which I could have done easily, I decided to project a huge image of the molecule. So these buckyballs are enormous, and we actually projected them here on the Department of Chemistry building, playing around with the idea of scale and that you can manipulate them with your shadow. In the molecular space, things don't work like they do in this space. It might look like a soccer ball, but it doesn't act like a soccer ball when you push it. And what was very striking to me is that I was told while I was moving it that if I push too hard, nothing is going to happen. That is interesting: you have to exert less force for something to happen. So in this design, when you go very slowly you can actually move the molecule; if you go fast, nothing happens, it just stays in place. As a result you have the audience slowing down – which became very much my intent from this point on.

Excerpt of the lecture "Art|Science Collaborations: Being in Between" on Wednesday, 16 June 2010

Tuesday, 22 June 2010

Oron Catts – Art Practice in the Form of "Tissue Culture"

Oron Catts is an artist, researcher, and curator. In 1996, he initiated the Tissue Culture & Art Project/TC&A. He is the co-founder and director of SymbioticA, The Centre of Excellence in Biological Arts, School of Anatomy and Human Biology, at the University of Western Australia. On Tuesday, 22 June 2010, he was invited by Professor Alfred Vendl in the course of a lecture series on "Science Visualization" to the University of Applied Arts Vienna. In the discussion after his presentation of his work the following questions were raised.

00:53:32.89

Q: What kind of cells were you using, for instance, for the *Worry Dolls*?

00:54:02.28

Oron Catts: Rather than travelling with cells from Australia, which is kind of difficult, we tend to make contact with a local laboratory whenever we are invited to show our work. This way of working started in the year 2000 when we said: "There's no way that this can be done in the States, there is no way we can travel with this." In any case, it is a part of our practice to intervene in the science world wherever we go. It is not enough for us to go to a gallery and interact with the artists – these interventions involve scientists as well.

In the case of the *Worry Dolls*, we were able to work with the virology department at the local hospital in Linz. We asked the scientist who hosted us to send us a list of all the cells he was working with – a list of about of 25 different cells. I must admit that my initial interest in the McCoy cell line had more to do with *Star Trek* than anything else, as I figured it would be really nice when the first tissue engineered sculptures we would present in the gallery would have the name of the first doctor McCoy. But then we did some research into literature and found a really interesting story about cells that were taken from a human but are now classified as those of a mouse. We thought this could also be a beautiful story for the *Worry Dolls* so we chose to work with them. And in the *Pig Wings* project, it was very important for us to work with pig tissue: we wanted to use multi-potent stem cells as we had a protocol on how to make them into bone. Then there are other projects such as a miniature version of growing of Stelarc's left ear where we used human cartilage cells for that purpose. So first of all, we use what is available in the places we are working with, but we also employ what is conceptually important for the work to succeed. In some cases, the choice of cells is less important; in other cases, it is essential.

00:55:57.12

Q: Where do you mainly show your work? In art galleries or in scientific environments as well?

00:56:10.08

OC: We show the work in quite a lot of different contexts. When we show the piece, it is usually in galleries and museums, everything from small places to the Museum of Modern Art in New York. That is quite a wide range. We also experimented with showing our work in science museums, which, in our opinion, wasn't really successful. We need to work on that. The science museum has an obligation to explain science to the audience, so people are more interested in that and less in the conceptual narrative in our work. So it can be quite problematic. And also the science museum, in most cases, has little interest to present the critical element of our work. But I give numerous talks to scientific audiences. I try to intervene in the scientific world and show them how their work – which they see as very trivial in some cases – is perceived by the public as something else. We don't really have the cultural tools to engage with what is going on in the labs. And when we speak of tissue culture, it is technology that is already a hundred years old and we still don't know how to deal with it as a culture. As artists, we try to engage with the scientists and with the wider community as well; we are trying to find out how to accomplish this and also identify the areas we need to pay more attention to.

00:58:11.09

Q: With regard to the materials of the living sculptures, how are they designed? How do you manipulate their shapes?

00:58:29.84

OC: We always work with a polymer scaffold; there are different ways in which we can give it a shape. The leather jacket (*Victimless Leather*), for example, is made out of a special polymer that is like fabric. It comes as a sheet of felt, small fibres pushed together into felt, into a material. We basically took the polymers and cut them into the form of the jacket. With the *Pig Wings* project, we created a mould, a negative shape of the wing, and then poured the polymer in it. What happened is not that it really grew in size rather we replaced the synthetic material of the polymer with living cells. As they grew in the bioreactor, within the environments we gave them, the polymer itself broke down and the cells took over the shape. With *Pig Wings* we were really successful because we did it over a period of eight months. The living tissue almost fully replaced the polymer. And since it was bone, it held the structure. With some of the *Worry Dolls* and some of the jackets this process happened in a few weeks, but even though the cells grew into the shape, there was no structure that held them together and they became these "blobs". It was interesting to see. And we never really know – there are so many factors involved, environmental factors, the polymer we are using, how fast it degrades. There are cells that we use each time, but when we grow them they behave somewhat differently, they grow faster, slower. Hence, we never know at the beginning how it will turn out in the end, when we present our piece in the gallery. We often receive phone calls from museums and gallery owners saying: "You know, your work looks different today than it did yesterday."

01:03:37.02

Q: You said you see yourself as an artist and art sometimes tries to push the limits. Therefore, I would like to ask why you request clearance from the ethical committee?

01:03:39.06

OC: They wouldn't let me do it otherwise.

01:03:41.48

Q: But could you do it otherwise? The laboratory as a place without consequence, keep your work in the laboratory… Did you ever consider pushing the limits as well? Because the ethical committee adds another layer of experts between other experts?

01:04:04.39

OC: As an individual artist I think I know enough now about how to set up my own lab in my backyard and do whatever I want. There is the story of Steve Kurtz from the United States who was arrested by the FBI because he had a laboratory, and they initially charged him with bioterrorism. My strategy is to work within the system because then I can get access to a lot of amazing resources. But also to be a subversive force from within, in a sense. It is not the only strategy, but it works very well for me because I'm also legit. An interesting thing about the ethical committee is that they give you a licence to do things that might otherwise be illegal. So when I take biopsies from artists – if I would go to you and cut out a piece of your skin tissue with a knife – I would be arrested for assault. If I get ethical approval to do it, I'm OK. So there are pluses and minuses regarding how to work with these ethics. Just recently, I had an ethics application that took me weeks and weeks to do. But in order for me to work within a structure, in a research centre, and for our research to be respected, I need to do these things.

01:05:38.92

Q: So it is a rigid framework?

01:05:56.93

OC: Yes, but to some extent that is also interesting. Artists, for instance, rarely have to make such justifications. And one of the questions from the ethical committee is how your work helps to benefit humanity. Most artists have ambitious goals, they want to save the world in a sense, but when you ask them how exactly this is going to happen they freak out. So you have to try to describe the work in such a way that is not just about how I'm going to be the biggest man in the world, rather you put it in ways so the ethical committee will allow you to do it. And that also changes the way people perceive the work. As you say, it is a rigid framework, but in the end the whole experience some of my artists had with the ethical committee became a large part of their work.

01:06:00.32

Q: Can you give us some ideas from your perspective about what is going on in the field of art and science?

01:06:40.96

OC: The field of art and science seems to be really picking up. Not only art and biology, but also other fields. And there are many different ways in which artists and scientists choose to work together or how artists engage with science. In many cases, it is still a realm where artists are using technology – even about 80% of our projects are really about artists using scientific technology; it is not about an involvement with science as such. With synthetic biology, for example, the European Union is now pouring millions and millions of euros into creating a public dialogue on this new technology. And some of that money goes towards artists. It can be good and it can be bad. We have to find out what it has to do with us. The human genome project tried to push a very strict agenda, but if artists are smart enough they can take the money and do something important with it. There are plenty of resources at the moment, especially in the area of new knowledge like synthetic biology and nanotechnology, where there is a push from above as well as from below. There is money there, but there is also a lot of interest and agendas, I think.

01:08:36.93

Q: Is there a kind of community, such as meetings around the globe, for example?

01:08:57.42

OC: Yes, there are quite a few. Again, I represent only a very small section, which is artists working in biology. When I started in 1996, there was virtually no one doing this kind of work. Now there are hundreds. At SymbioticA, if you think about the more than 70 residencies and the participation in the workshops, there are about 300 to 400 people. Other centres are emerging around the globe. There is the Ectopia laboratory in Lisbon and the Art and Genomics Centre in Leiden. And now we are starting to have those meetings. Up to now, we tended to be closer to electronic arts. There are quite a few works that have been shown at Ars Electronica; there is the Inter-Society for the Electronic Arts (ISEA) that hosted a number of sessions about artistic work in biology – but these were the very same people that couldn't handle Tagny Duff's work with viruses, and she couldn't show her work as part of the conference. This raises the importance of establishing something that is dedicated to this type of activity. We are actually setting up a society in our region for science, literature, and the arts, where there will be a conference in 2013. There are lots and lots of movements.

01:09:12.96

Q: Isn't there a problem with this popularisation of scientific knowledge? Are you perhaps sometimes accused of propagating science? I'm coming back to the framework problem: If you get the money, you do it, but as soon as you break the rules of those who pay you then it becomes really weird.

01:10:58.04

OC: This is something we have to be very careful about because it is very tempting. For example, I was happy when the *Pig Wings* project was rejected – and rejected in such a nasty way – when we submitted it for an exhibition celebrating the, so-called, completion of the first draft of the human genome project. We knew then that we were doing something right.

They actually tried to sue us because we published the whole exchange with them on our website. It is a very fine line. And even in our work, critical projects are then reappropriated. Once your art is in the public domain, it can be reappropriated and used. At a recent conference in Riga, we had a call for action to deal with what is going on in synthetic biology. It is one of the first technologies in which there is a very direct move to engineer public acceptance even before the technology is there. I have been to some meetings where it was said that we have to learn from genetic engineering; we have to create public acceptance before we push it. And the solution was to use artists. But, on the other hand, I also think there is a community of artists who are sophisticated enough and have the experience to try to manipulate this. It might not work, but we need to address such issues and I think these areas need cultural scrutiny. One way to do it – and I don't say it is the only one – is from within.

Excerpt of discussion after the lecture "Art Practice in the Form of 'Tissue Culture'" on Tuesday, 22 June 2010

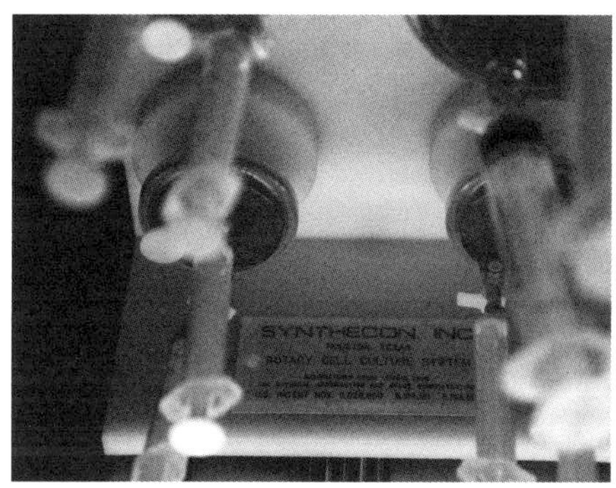

Tom Holert Joint Ventures. On the State of Collaboration

Holert, Tom. Joint Ventures: The State of Collaboration.
Artforum International Magazine (February 2011), 158–161.

The utopia of truly shared, communal, multiple authorship always seems to be receding from sight. But the dream won't die: Collaboration continues to be held up as a means of escaping Western, patriarchal mythology and power structures as well as the art-market matrix of originality and authorship. Collectives and collaboratives are still assumed to be intrinsically liberating. Their emancipatory dimension is linked with the elevation of co-labor, of working in teams rather than lingering in the solitude of the studio. According to Mira Schor, the feminist artist and former co-editor of the journal *M/E/A/N/I/N/G*, the particular activation of the individual immersed in a collective with a shared goal entails "a peculiar relief in going outside the self".[1]

Collaborative and collectivist practices have historically enabled alternative modes of subjectivity; in the best case, they promise to open up divergent routes of being-with-others while subverting the ruling regimes of visibility and representation. Such aspirations made them central to the many feminist, queer, postcolonial, and antiracist cultural practices that became more and more active and visible in the 1970s and '80s, accompanying the rediscovery in those years of the historical avant-gardes, from the Fauves to Dada to Russian Productivism. Self-organized, alternative spaces, co-op galleries, etc. also emerged on the grounds of new insights into asymmetrical power relations.

Indeed, the analysis of power from the angle of identity (and, ultimately, anti-identitarian) politics relies on the involvement of specific communities rather than individuals. A hegemonic group – for example, that of white male artists – can be contested by a practice of collaboration that confronts ostensibly naturalized power with critical solidarity. Art historian and theorist Irit Rogoff has written (specifically with reference to the Guerrilla Girls and Tim Rollins and K.O.S.) that collectivity not only ruptures the authority of "the artist" but also brings about "the emergence of an author grounded in the collective and social politics of identity formation rather than in the traditional and rarefied realm of identity affirmation".[2]

Along similar lines, Vietnamese filmmaker, writer, and theorist Trinh T. Minh-ha – who in her own practice has always dealt, if implicitly, with the relations between collectivities, constituencies, and subjectivities – has pointed out that the "tendency to value collaborative work over individual work [occurs] in contexts where it is almost impossible to escape the burden of representation".[3] As examples of groups in which "a certain rejection of individual authorship may thrive", Trinh mentions the UK film groups Sankofa and Black Audio Film Collective (BAFC). Shedding light on another aspect of collective practice, John Akomfrah, a cofounder of BAFC, in 1983 stressed its importance as a strategy to "de-mystify [...] the process of film production"; moreover, his hope was that it "would also involve collapsing the distinction between 'audience' and 'producer'".[4] According to this view, which harks back to Constructivist and Productivist models, collectivity becomes a methodology for transforming both the reception of an artwork and its production. It's not surprising that film, as an inherently collaborative mode of cultural production, features prominently as a medium of collective artmaking from the margins.

Nevertheless, as Trinh also argues, many groups – particularly those that act as collectives of production – tend to organize themselves hierarchically in spite of themselves, granting leadership to whoever has the most compelling plan or vision (or, simply, whoever has more social or economic power). In consequence of this and other caveats, she rethinks the notion of collaboration, proposing that it "happens not when something common is shared between the collaborators, but when something that belongs to neither of them comes to pass between them".[5] This something in between could be defined as the contingent product or outcome of a given collaboration that retroactively emerges as constitutive of the shared project or enterprise. As Trinh sees it, collaboration is thus essentially unintentional; it cannot be planned or anticipated.

This dynamic of will and contingency, individual and group, resonates with a question in Martha Rosler's contribution to the 1982 Documenta catalogue: "Was it a struggle within and without, inside the group, against it as well as for it, for a perhaps only utopian collaborativeness-in-general, to occasion individual freedom?"[6] In that same text, Rosler describes "the fashion for cooperation" as having "faded" by the end of the '70s. What I would call a "tribal" spirit followed, instigated by punk and New/No Wave and by a newly discovered sensibility of underground primitivism. The idea of community was at this time far less wedded to the political – even though many of the loose, hedonistic, and implicitly oppositional neo-bohemianisms of the '80s eventually linked up with the new politics of aids activism and postcolonial struggles. Writing in 1991, artist Josef Strau considered collectivity as a kind of historical relic, speaking of "leftover models" and "a spirit of well-known, historically bankrupt, wannabe significant ideas of exchange and distribution (co-operatives, networks etc.)", whose remainders he and his partner, Stephan Dillemuth, were about to "restore" in their Cologne artists' bar/gallery space Friesenwall 120 – also as a means of testing the conditions of the art system from a position of self-imposed marginality.[7]

Strau's plea for a methodical revisiting of abandoned practices of collaboration and political activism indicates both the difficulty and the potential of collectivity in the arts at the beginning of the '90s. In Europe, a revival of cooperative art production followed – and particularly of exhibition making, exemplified by institutions such as Shedhalle Zurich and Kunst-Werke in Berlin. The real return of collaboration and cooperation, however, was arguably in the 2000s, with a host of activities, exhibitions, and publications on the issue itself, however broadly defined. To sketch a potted history using a few keywords from that decade, the "participatory challenge"[8] led to "relational aesthetics"[9] and "conversation pieces",[10] which in turn engendered "taking the matter into common hands".[11] There were also warnings from quarters skeptical of this resurgence, however – not least critic Claire Bishop in her article in these pages on collaboration's "discontents".[12] (Many of these conversations actually revolved around participation and interaction with audiences, rather than addressing a disturbance or multiplication of authorship from the outset.)

The fundamentally "collective" character of capitalist production, stressed repeatedly in Marx's Capital, is today increasingly reflected in the systemic or even ontological "collaborativity" of networked cultures, constituted as they are by the immaterial and mostly unpaid labor of participants across the world – whether they are uploading images to the Web, writing on a newspaper comment board, or rating books on Amazon. As collaboration has become generalized, a reassessment of the past and present status of the collective as a form of the social organization of cultural production is crucial. Arguably, the practice of collectivity could offer an alternative to the contemporary governmentality that wants the individual to be both the singular performer of a spectacular self and the obedient and functioning team player. Collective forms might even enable the pursuit of otherwise socially and technologically predetermined aspects of collaboration in a more direct, material, and urgent manner. Blake Stimson and Gregory Sholette, the editors of *Collectivism After Modernism*, speak of a new "dream of collectivism," a "fetish" that can still offer activist efficacy. They describe it as "neither the strategic vision of some future ideal" nor "the mobile, culture-jamming, more-mediated-than-thou counterhegemony of collectivism after modernism", but the engagement "with social life itself as the medium of expression".[13]

At the same time, though, it would be a mistake to treat the collective as invariably superior to less group-oriented modes of artistic operation. Working in a collective framework does not automatically lead to a critical stance toward the mechanics of originality and individuality: Performing as a member of a group can, for instance, easily become the precondition of an individual artist's success. The collaboration between protagonists from different fields has also, in the name of academic interdisciplinarity, turned into an imperative for every creative production aspiring to qualify as "innovative research" deemed worthy of government funding. When being able to work well with others and an unconditional openness to difference and diversity are deeply embedded in capitalist notions of the team-playing self, aspirations to collectivity are an ambiguous good. Not least for this reason, we should be wary when artists choose (or are chosen for) a collaborative mode of operation today – even if (to borrow the words of New York-based artist-run "platform" 16 Beaver Group) this is done in order "to take our inquiries beyond self-interest and contribute to this pool that some have called the general intellect".[14]

The nostalgia for rare, bygone moments of collective accomplishment still feeds a hope of overcoming, if only temporarily, prevailing patterns of depoliticization. Yet we must remember that each reinvocation and resignification of collaboration and collectivity, as well as any corresponding (self-)criticism, is a response to mutations of the spaces of the political and the possibilities of articulation within and beyond these spaces. One of 16 Beaver's founders, the artist Rene Gabri, explains why collaboration should not be thought of outside present political upheavals: "I cannot think of new artworlds [...] without implicitly thinking about new worlds." Arguing that practices that are considered collective, social, collaborative, or participatory often "do more to hide differences and disagreement than they do to confront or reveal them", he speaks of the collectivity we now need as having to offer "something beyond the kind of social cooperation we have been presented under capitalism".[15]

Collaboration is in danger of losing its disruptive potential, since the novel forms of subjectification it nurtures have either been co-opted already or are at risk of being so: It is the "terms", as Gabri puts it, and not the mere fact of cooperation, that are today at stake. To find feasible ways of teaming up and working together – ways that go beyond those by which individuals continually and inevitably contribute to and cooperate in culture today – requires a double move. It demands both an acute awareness of the abstract logic that determines the constant appropriation of social and psychic energies by capital, and a willingness to engage with the concrete micropolitics of material, social practices whose outcomes are often unintentional and can never be predicted. In other words, cooperation is a kind of ethics. Now it needs to be wrested from the historical conditions that shaped it in the first place.

1
Mira Schor, "On Creativity and Community", *M/E/A/N/I/N/G*, 15 (1994), reprinted in *M/E/A/N/I/N/G: An Anthology of Artists' Writings, Theory, and Criticism*, ed. Susan Bee and Mira Schor (Durham, NC: Duke University Press, 2000), 337.

2
Irit Rogoff, "Production Lines," *Team Spirit*, ed. Susan Sollins and Nina Castelli Sundell (New York: Independent Curators Incorporated, 1990), 39. Accessible online at *http://collabarts.org/?p=69*.

3
Gwendolyn Foster, "A Tale of Love: A Dialogue with Trinh T. Minh-ha", *Film Criticism* 21, no. 3 (Spring 1997), quoted in Trinh T. Minh-ha, *Cinema Interval* (New York: Routledge, 1999), 244.

4
John Akomfrah, "Black Independent Film-Making: A Statement by the Black Audio Film/Video Collective", *Artrage: Inter Cultural Arts Magazine* 3/4 (Summer 1983): 29, quoted in Manthia Diawara, "Power and Territory: The Emergence of Black British Film Collectives", *Fires Were Started: British Cinema and Thatcherism*, 2nd ed., ed. Lester D. Friedman (London: Wallflower Press, 1996), 129.

5
Quoted in Trinh, *Cinema Interval*, 244.

6
Martha Rosler, *Documenta 7*, exh. cat., vol. 2 (D+V Paul Dierichs: Kassel, 1982), 284.

7
Josef Strau, "Friesenwall 120", *Texte zur Kunst 2* (Spring 1991): 174-75.

8
Trebor Scholz, "The Participatory Challenge", *DATA Browser 03: Curating Immateriality; the Work of the Curator in the Age of Network Systems*, ed. Joasia Krysa (New York: Autonomedia, 2006), 195–213.

9
Nicolas Bourriaud, *Esthétique relationelle* (Dijon, France: Les Presses, du réel, 2002).

10
Grant H. Kester, *Conversation Pieces: Community and Communication in Modern Art* (Berkeley: University of California Press, 2004).

11
Johanna Billing, Maria Lind, and Lars Nilsson (eds.), *Taking the Matter into Common Hands: On Contemporary Art and Collaborative Practices* (London: Black Dog Publishing, 2007).

12
Claire Bishop, "The Social Turn: Collaboration and Its Discontents", *Artforum*, February 2006, 178–83.

13
Blake Stimson and Gregory Sholette, introduction to *Collectivism After Modernism: The Art of Social Imagination After 1945* (Minneapolis: University of Minnesota Press, 2007), 13.

14
16 Beaver Group, "Continental Drift: Introduction I", 2006, *http://www.16beavergroup.org/drift/intro2006ny*.

15
Rene Gabri, "Postscript from Rene", in Billing, Lind, and Nilsson, *Taking the Matter into Common Hands*, 127–28

Theoretical Flotsam & Jetsam, Open-Air Seminar
Michel Serres's *The Parasite* provided the inspiration for collecting and ordering, walking and talking, relating and tinkering. Parasites of various kind and different ontological status; the Danube as background noise and surprising signals in our hands: beyond yes and no; quasi-objects as trophies brought back home. Encountering animals in fables and other worlds. First and foremost the rats: test animals and research subjects. They turn the view back to ourselves. However, sometimes we have to eat.

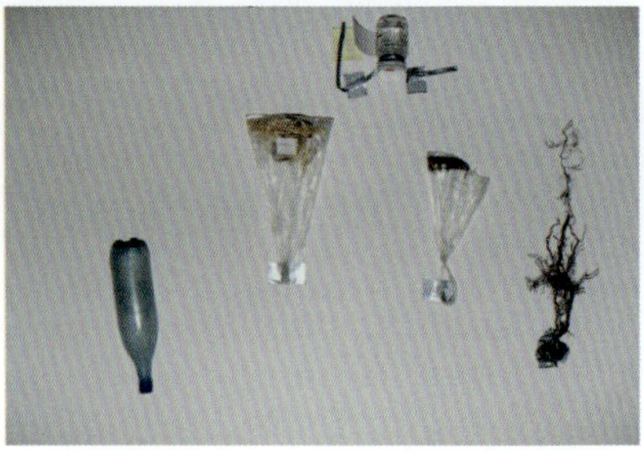

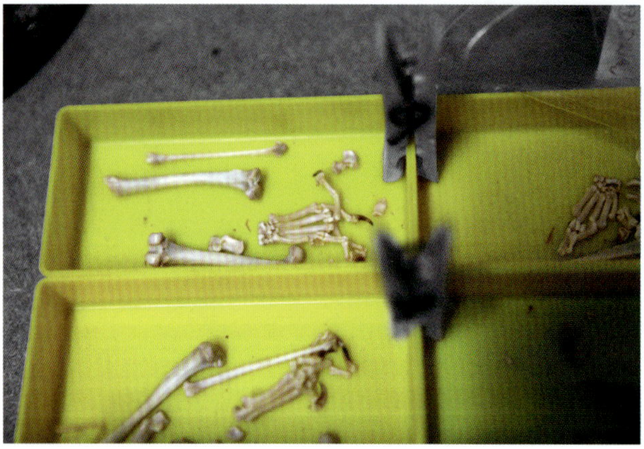

Sabina Teichert, Question – About Care

During a project work in 2010, twenty non-European flies ended up in our space at the university in Vienna. Their arrival was unexpected, but now they were here and I had the feeling I have to take care of them. I wanted to make a film while they are having sex, so it was in my interest that they survived their days at the school until they were delivered to the experts at the biouniversity. As I had read papers and done research on the species, I knew that they have to be fed with blood.

I must be honest and admit that initially I didn't even think about it. But after a day I started to become concerned. So I went to a Turkish butcher and asked for some fresh meat that was still bloody. That's how I got beef liver. Satisfied, I took the stuff back to school and tried to figure out how I would feed the flies.

Everything I did was wrong. The temperature, the missing membrane, etc., etc.

But at the point when I attempted this action I was truly concerned; the flies had become like family members to me. This made me really think about care. After that, the flies died or were killed in the lab. Actually, the entire research I was dealing with was about eradicating the population on the long term because they cause harm to humans.

A few weeks later, I was on the countryside; it was very hot, and there were many, many flies. I was really disturbed by them and began to strike them dead, one by one.

A year later in a science lab, I was again confronted with such a scenario – namely not knowing what to do. The situation of having to make a decision but having a choice as well: what to do?

Artist in the lab. I had lunch in the staff canteen. In the manner I had learned at American salad bars, I systematically layered all kinds of antipasti on my empty plate from the bottom up and topped it off with a blanket of green salad leaves. It took me about an hour to absorb this quantity. In the meanwhile, I looked around and listened.

Back in the lab. The vote about the mouse. Shall we do our lab work with dead meat or shall we make our investigation and research with an animal that will be killed for this purpose? In-between, a lot of explanations, arguments, varying perceptions, and other complexities. There was one thing aside from all of this, which made it easy for me to instantly make a decision (not to speak about right or wrong): it was my inner voice speaking, which said no. It was a big help for me, to trust myself at that moment, nevertheless still knowing: I don't know the answer. "Reality", what a concept? How can I learn about it, how can I know?

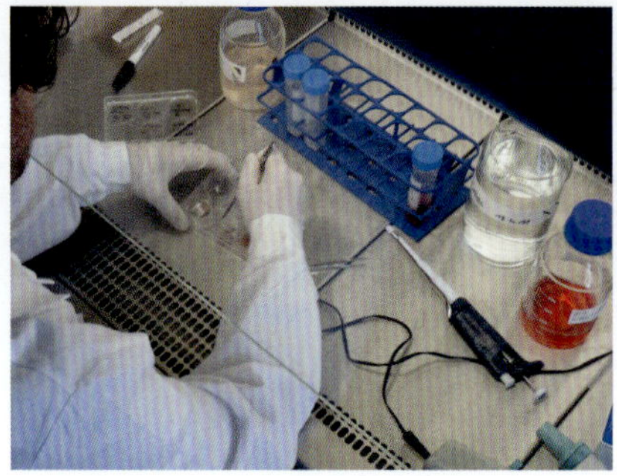

IMBA, Dr. Bohr-Gasse 3, 1030 Vienna, 9 May 2011

Day 1

Introduction to Bioart and Basic Cell and Tissue Culture 9.30–10.00, Plaza Lounge: Informal 'Meet and Greet' Session. 10.00–10.30, Seminar Room 5.14: Introduction to Bioart and Working with Cell Lines 10.30–11.00, Plaza Lounge: Tea Break, Relocation to Laboratory 11.00–12.00, Laboratory: Health and Safety / Lab Induction 12.00–13.00, Cafeteria Lunch 13.00–15.00, Laboratory: Introduction to Cell and Tissue Culture 15.00–15.30, Plaza Lounge: Tea Break 15.30–17.00, Seminar Room 6.20: Introduction to Microscopy with Pawel Pasierbek

Day 2–4

Preparing Media. Thawing Frozen Cells. Prepare Scaffolds from Clinical and Non-Clinical Material. Agar Plate Preparation.

Day 5

Genetic Engineering – Seeing The Glowing Outcome and Discussion Forum Translating Science Into Art 9.30–10.30: From Science To Art 10.30–11.00: Tea Break and Relocation to Laboratory 11.00–12.00: pGLO Bacteria UV Exposure and Cell Check 13.00–15.00: Wrap Up, Freezing and Disposal of Workshop Materials 15.00–15.30: Tea Break 15.30–17.00: Discussion Session / Creative Ideas Generation.

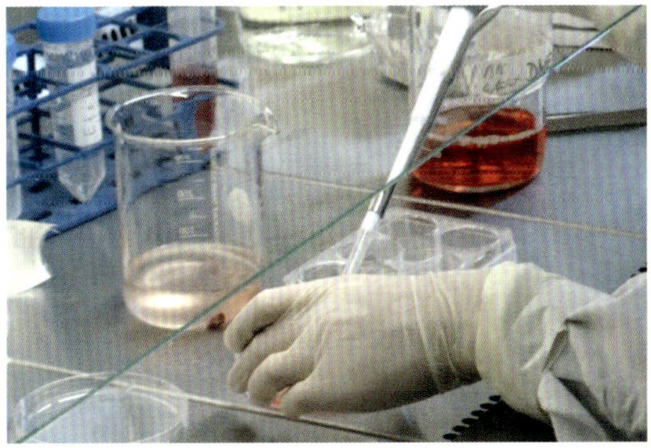

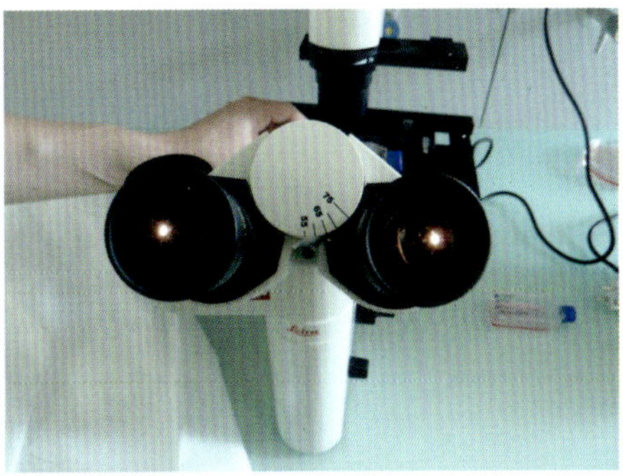

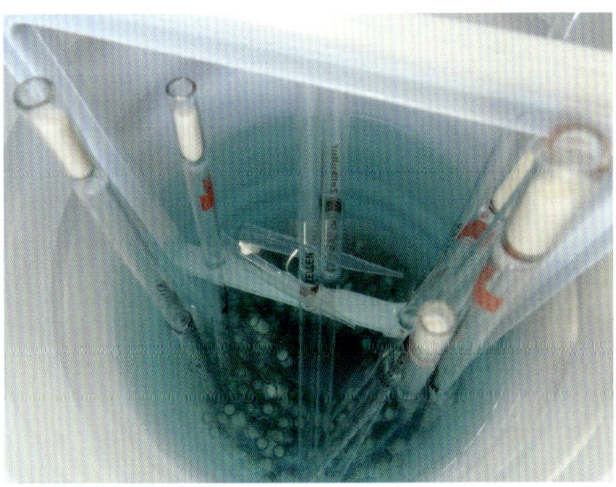

Anna Fatér, Vegetarian Meat – Semi-Living Food

On the third day of the workshop "Biotechnology and Contemporary Art" by Svenja Kratz at the Institute of Molecular Biotechnology Vienna, we engaged in an experiment that relates to a project of Oron Catts and Ionat Zurr, *Disembodied Cuisine*. It deals with the ethics of food consumption and how the distinction is made between food and non-food. We were asked to bring fresh meat to the laboratory, meat as fresh as possible.

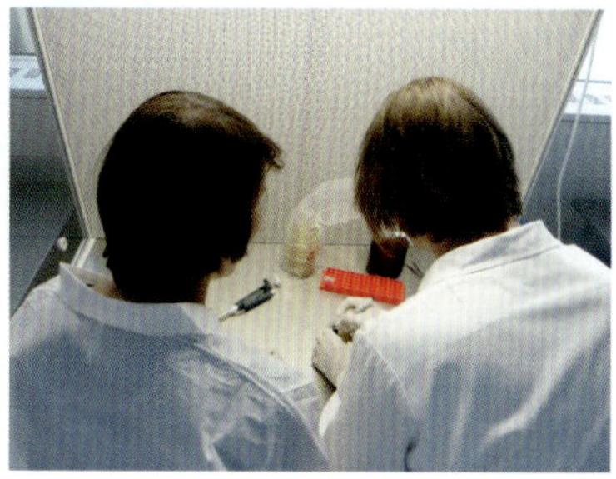

First of all, the meat was needed for isolating primary animal cells. Once the animal tissue had been swabbed with ethanol, a tiny section was removed and immersed again in ethanol. Then it was transported to the hood where it was covered with phosphate buffered saline (PBS) a few times. It was possible to continue in two ways: either to add 1mL of Trypsin or to add 1mL of collagenase solution. The tissue samples were then minced and more (9mL) of the respective liquid was added. Subsequently, the minced samples were dispersed with a sterile pipette to further break them up and aid tissue digestion. Discarded leftover tissue fragments and new, warm medium topped off the mixture with the cells. After the flasks were labelled with the name, date, and type of cells, they were placed in an incubator.

From the meat that was brought to the lab (whole lamb livers, huge pieces of salmon, arms of octopi) only really tiny parts were used for the cell work. To make use of the left over parts, Svenja initially planned to prepare a lunch. She asked us to bring spices and other ingredients to cook it together. Ultimately, the cooking never happened as we ran out of time on that particular day. But the imagination of eating the meat – meat that was once in a lab – still had an impact. It felt as if the meat had somehow become unclean, which is an interesting thought as everything in the lab is sterile.

In this regard, we started to deal with similar questions that *Disembodied Cuisine* brought up – but with a little difference: we were trying to keep alive the cells of a dead animal, not grow cells of still living animals. We planned to eat the parts of an animal already "intended for eating", to use it as a material that can also be used for scientific purposes.

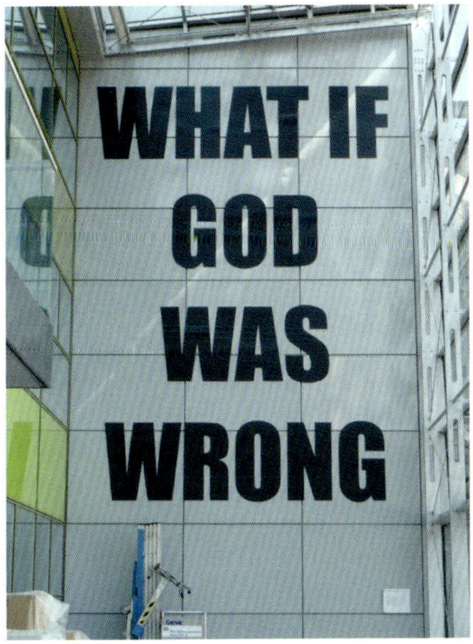
WHAT IF
GOD
WAS
WRONG

ARTSCIENCE

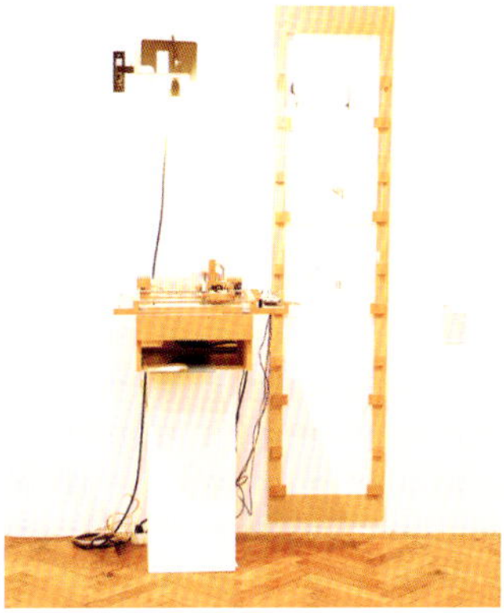

In the course of a year, from fall 2010 until summer 2011, two workshops were held on the software Processing (www.processing.org). Students were taught the basics of algorithmic image creation and encouraged to put the tools to use in expressing some of their own ideas. Two posters were created depicting the results.

```
int i = 0;                          //Variable, ganze Zahlen
PImage a;                           //Variable Bild
int bildzahl = 83;                  //Variable Bildzahl, ganze Zahlen
float abstand;                      //Variable Abstand, auch Kommazahlen

void setup () {
  size (1000,500);                  //Größe des Bildes
  abstand = width/bildzahl;         //Länge durch Anzahl der Bilder (83)
  println (abstand);                //schreibt den Abstand unten ins schwarze Feld
}
void draw () {
    a = loadImage (i+1021+ ".JPG");           //Laden der Bilder
    image (a, i * abstand, 0, abstand, height);
                                    //a für das Bild,  x (0*Abstand(width/bildzahl))

//vom Bild, y vom Bild ist immer 0, Hineinzeichnen in die Länge Abstand und Breite Height

  i = i +1;                         //nimmt aufeinanderfolgend nummerierte Bilder
  if (i ==bildzahl) {               //endet wenn alle einmal gezeichnet wurden
    noLoop ();
  }
  saveFrame ("bildzahl-####.png");            //speichert die Bildserie
}
```

Brigitte Zwick \\ Reifungsprozess

```
// 0... linen
// 1... rechtecke
// 2... cooller pinsel
int tool = 0;
//---------------------------------------
float angle = 0;
float angleSpeed = 1;
int signum= 1;
int maxAngle= 100;
PVector[] dots = new PVector[maxAngle+1];
int laengeLine = 250;

void PendelBrush(){
    translate(mouseX, mouseY),
// dynamisch falls ich size ändern würde
    rotate(radians(angle));
    stroke(5);
//   line(0,0,laengeLine,0);
    dots [(int)angle]  = new
PVector(laengeLine, 0);
//     point (laengeLine, 0);
    angle = angle + signum*angleSpeed;
     if(angle == maxAngle){
      signum = -1;
     }
     if(angle == 0){
       signum = 1;
```

Benjamin Urbanek \\ Paint 2000

```
//Programm das die einzelnen Pixel aus jeder Uhrzeit ausliest
//und zu einem Bild kopiert;
//mit mehreren Pixeln aus einem Bild, damit es schneller geht
//Teilung von A3
int X = 1;
//Anzahl Bilder
int z = 1440;
int count = 0;
int y = 1;
int ziffer = 1;
int index = 0;
//int[] numbers = new int[width*height];
PImage render;
void setup(){
size (4692/X,1398/X);
background (255);
render = loadImage("weiss.png");
//for (int no = 0; no < width*height; no++) {
//numbers[no] = no;
//}
}
void draw() {
PImage zeit = loadImage("C:/Dokumente und Einstellungen/Tristan/
Desktop/Zeitraf
//ziffer = int(random(1,z));
render.loadPixels();
for (int i = 0; i <= (width*height)/z; i++) {
index = int(random(width*height));
//index = int(random((width*height)-count));
//numbers[index] = (height*width)-count;
render.pixels[index] = zeit.pixels[index];
render.updatePixels();
print (ziffer);
print (", ");
//print (i);
//print (", ");
print (index);
print (", ");
println (y);
}
image (render,0,0);
saveFrame("time_gr" + ziffer + ".png");
ziffer = ziffer + 1;
if (ziffer == z) {
noLoop();
//saveFrame("time_gr" + y + ".png");
// ziffer = 0;
// y = y+1;
// render = loadImage("weiss.png");
}
}
```

Richard Schwarz \\ Alle Zeit des Tages

```
PVector v1, v2;
int ballis = 1000;
int i = 0;
float radius = 7;
PVector alt = new PVector ();
PVector neu = new PVector ();

void setup () {
  size (500, 500);
  background (255);
  smooth ();
  //frameRate(2);
 alt = new PVector(random
(0,500),random (0,500));
}

void draw () {
  println(i);

  neu = new PVector(random
(0,500),random (0,500));
  nachbar (alt, neu, radius);

    float transparency = ran-
dom (0, 50);

    fill(0,0,0, 20);
    ellipse(alt.x,alt.y,radi
us,radius);
    alt = neu;

 // nachbar (M[0], M[1]);
 // nachbar (M[1], M[2]);
 // nachbar (M[2], M[3]);
 // nachbar (M[3], M[4]);
 // nachbar (M[4], M[5]);
 // nachbar (M[5], M[6]);
 // nachbar (M[6], M[7]);
 // loop ();
 // frameRate (5);
}

void nachbar (PVector P0,
PVector P1, float abstand) {
  PVector v01= PVector.
sub(P1,P0);
  v01.normalize();
  v01.mult(abstand);
  P1.x = P0.x;
  P1.y = P0.y;
  P1.add(v01);
}
```

Waltraud Scharfmüller \\ Agentenwachstum

```
/*
collage generator. example footage can be found in "_4_2_1_footage". if
you use your own footage, make sure to rename the files or
adjust the prefixes: see the parameters of generateCollageItems()KEYS
1-3 : create a new collage (layer specific) s : save png
*/

PImage[] images;
String[] imageNames;
int imageCount;

CollageItem[] layer1Items, layer2Items, layer3Items;

void setup() {
  size(1920, 1080);
  imageMode(CENTER);
  background(0);

/* ------ load images ------
replace this location with a folder on your machine or use selectFolder()
  File dir = new  File(selectFolder("choose a folder with collage footage
...")); File dir = new File(sketchPath,"../_4_2_1_footage");
*/

if (dir.isDirectory()) {
 String[] contents = dir.list();
 images = new PImage[contents length];
```

Sabina Teichert \\ Collage

```
package agents;
/*
 * @author mlg
 */
import processing.core.*;
//import static process-
ing.core.PConstants.*;
import static agents.
AgentSim.*;

class Agent {
    static int count = 0;
PApplet p;
int id;
float direction = 1;
float speed = 1;
PVector pos;
int birthday;
float size = 1;
int col;
boolean fem;
int maturity;
int children = 0;
float lifeEx;
    int max_children;
    boolean sterile =
false;

    Agent(float posx, float
posy, float direction, PAp-
plet p) {
        this(posx, posy,
direction, p, FEM_CHANCE,
false, ROBUSTNESS, MATU-
RITY, FERTILITY, SPEEDI-
NESS);
    }
    Agent(float posx, float
posy, float direction, PAp-
plet p, float fem_chance,
boolean sterile, float
robustness, float matu-
rity, float fertility, float
speediness) {
        this.p = p;
        this.pos = new
PVector(posx, posy);
        this.birthday =
p.frameCount;
        this.id = ++Agent.
count;
        this.direction =
direction;
        this.col =
p.color(255);
        this.fem =
(p.random(1) < fem_
chance);
```

Martin Gródl \\ Catch Me Fly

```
/*
1000 Messwerte - 1000 Meisterwerke
Leon Ploszczanski
08.06.2010
Version 0.2
Arduino leitet Werte an ein Array, daß in Graphform
und als Textdateiausgegeben wird.
In der Testversion ist die Arduinolibrary noch mit
einer Randomfunktion als Platzhalter substituiert.
v
*/

float spacing = 1.75;
ArrayList werte;
PrintWriter output;

void setup (){

    size (1920 , 1000);
    background (0);
    fill (0);
    smooth();
    stroke (random(100,255), random(100,255), ran-
dom(100,255));
    loop();
```

Leon Ploszczanski \\ Messreihe

```
PVector v1, v2;
int ballis = 1000;
int i = 0;
float radius = 7;
PVector alt = new PVector ();
PVector neu = new PVector ();

void setup () {
  size (500, 500);
  background (255);
  smooth ();
  //frameRate(2);
 alt = new PVector(random (0,500),ran-
dom (0,500));

}

void draw () {
  println(i);

  neu = new PVector(random (0,500),ran-
dom (0,500));
  nachbar (alt, neu, radius);

    fill(0,0,0, 20);
    stroke(0, 0, 0, 20*2);
    ellipse(alt.x,alt.y,radius,radius);
    alt = neu;

 // nachbar (M[0], M[1]);
 // nachbar (M[1], M[2]);
 // nachbar (M[2], M[3]);
 // nachbar (M[3], M[4]);
 // nachbar (M[4], M[5]);
 // nachbar (M[5], M[6]);
 // nachbar (M[6], M[7]);
 // loop ();
 // frameRate (5);
}

void nachbar (PVector P0, PVector P1,
float abstand) {
  PVector v01= PVector.sub(P1,P0);
  v01.normalize();
  v01.mult(abstand);
  P1.x = P0.x;
  P1.y = P0.y;
  P1.add(v01);
}
```

Wolfgang Schwarzenbrunner \\ Pink Spiro

Beniamin Urbanek // Paint 2000
Brigitte Zwick / Reifungsprozess
Richard Schwarz // Alle Zeit des Tages
Sabina Teichert // Collage
Waltraud Schartmüller // Agentenwachstum
Martin Grödl // Catch Me Fly
Wolfgang Schwarzenbrunner // Pink Spiro
Leon Ploszczanski // Messreihe

Sarah Duit // Black_and_White

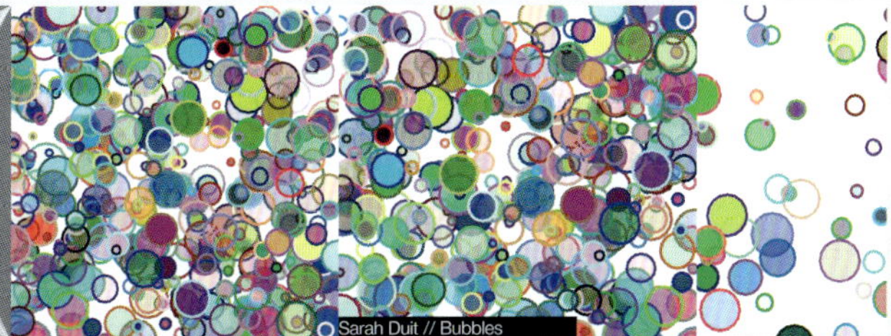

Sarah Duit // Bubbles

Richard Schwarz // Panorama_rs

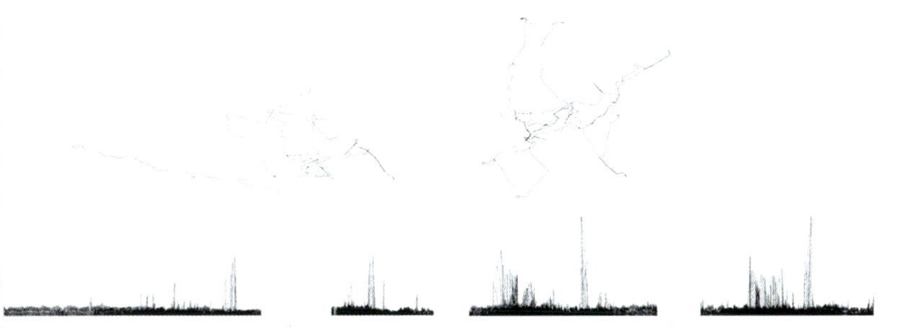

Ashley Holwell, Romana Egatner // JonnyPrint

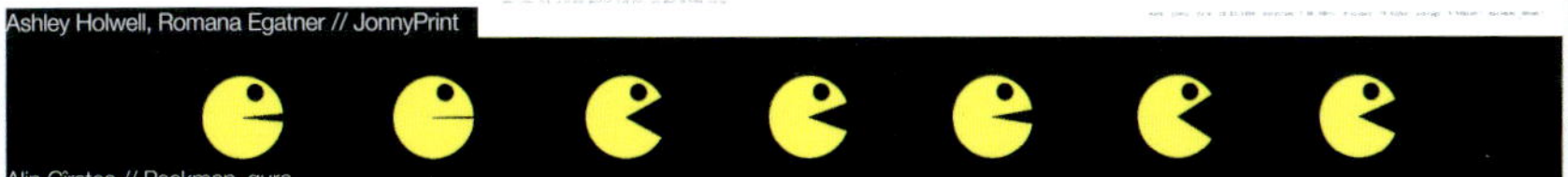

Alin Cîrstea // Packman_gura

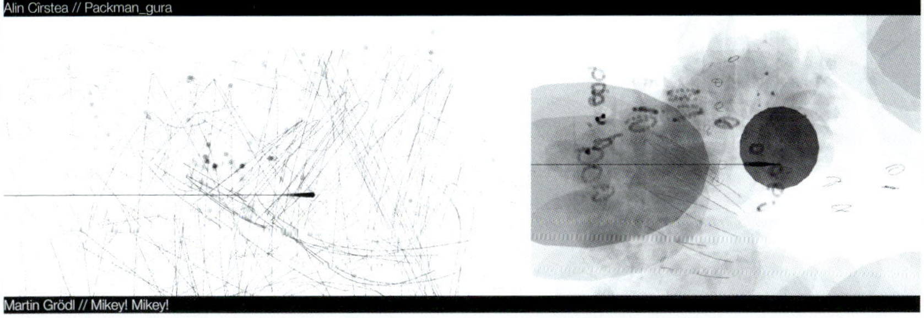

Martin Grödl // Mikey! Mikey!

```
void setup ()
{
  size (500, 500);
  background (255);
  frameRate (10);
}

void draw ()
{
  fill (random (0, 255), random (0, 255), random (0, 255), random (0, 255));
  stroke (random (0, 255), random (0, 255), random (0, 255));

  strokeWeight (4);

  float size = random (10, 60);

  ellipse (random (0, width), random (0, height), size, size);

  if (keyPressed && key == 's')
  {
    saveFrame ("image");
    println ("image saved");
  }
}
```

Sarah Duit \\ Bubbles

```
void setup ()
{
  size (800,
800);
}

void draw ()
{
  fill (100, 1);
  rect (0, 0,
width, height);

  if (mouse-
Pressed && mouse-
Button == LEFT)
  {
    stroke (220);
  }
  else if (mouse-
Pressed && mouse-
Button == RIGHT)
  {
    stroke (80);
  }
  else
  {
    noStroke ();
  }

    line (mouseX,
mouseY, 0, 0);
    line (mouseX,
mouseY, 0,
height);
    line (mouseX,
mouseY, width,
0);
    line (mouseX,
mouseY, width,
height);

    if (keyPressed
&& key == 's')
    {
      saveFrame
("image");
      println ("im
```

Sarah Duit \\ Black_and_White

```
//Dateien laden

import java.io.File;
import java.io.FilenameFilter;
import java.io.FileFilter;

String dirName;
String[] bildName;

File dir;

int idx;//anzahl bilder im
Ordner
int nummer = 1000; //bildnummer
int x_kord = 1;//x-position
von bild
int frame = 0;

PImage teil;
PImage pixel;
int ausschnitt = 4;//bei höherer
geschwindigkeit 29px

void setup()
{

  dirName = selectFolder();

  dir = new File(dirName);

  ordnerSuche(dir);

  teil =
loadImage(bildName[0]);

  size(10000, teil.height);

}

void draw()
{
  pixel = teil.get(0, 0, aus-
schnitt, height);

  image(pixel, width-(x_
kord*ausschnitt), 0);

  nummer++;
  x_kord++;

  teil =
loadIage(bildName[nummer]);

  if (x_kord*ausschnitt > width)
  {
    saveFrame("output/panorama_"
+ frame + "_" + ausschnitt +
".png");
    x_kord = 1;
    nummer = 1000;
    ausschnitt++;
    frame++;
  }

  if (ausschnitt > 40)
  {
    noLoop();
  }

  println(nummer);
}

  void ordnerSuche(File dir) {

    File[] files = dir.listFiles();

    if (files != null) {

      bildName = new String[files.
length];

      idx = files.length;

      println(files.length);

      for (int i = 0; i < idx;
i++) {

        if (files[i].getName().
toLowerCase().endsWith(".
jpg")) {
          bildName[i] = files[i].
getPath();
          println("i = " + i);
```

Richard Schwarz \\ Panorama_rs

```
String[] jonnyTrack;

float waypointDistance;

float lastLatitude;
float lastLongitude;

float maxWaypointDistance = 0;
float minWaypointDistance = 0;
float maxLongitude = 0;
float minLongitude = 100;
float maxLatitude = 0;
float minLatitude = 100;

float positionX = 0;
float positionY = 0;
float lastPositionX = 0;
float lastPositionY = 0;

// adjust here for playback speed
float maxdelay = 200;

// print out data values as we draw? (might
slow down the animation)
boolean printData = false;

// for each index holds: 0..longitude,
1..latitude, 2..distance (= diff to last
coordinates)
float[][] jonnyWaypoints;

// lat :  y
// long:  x
// vienna: lat:48° 15' North and long:16°
22' East
// data file: long(x),lat(y),elevation/...
void setup() {

  jonnyTrack = loadStrings("jonny_1_raw.
txt");
  //jonnyTrack = loadStrings("jonny_2_raw.
txt");
  //jonnyTrack = loadStrings("jonny_3_raw.
txt");
  //jonnyTrack = loadStrings("jonny_4_raw.
txt");

  size(1000, 600);

  background(255);
  stroke(0, 100); // use transparent stroke
so line gets darker when he stays in one
point
  strokeWeight(1);

  /*
  // try these settings to see stops re-
ally well
  stroke(0, 10); // use transparent stroke
so line gets darker when he stays in one
point
  strokeWeight(10);
  */

  smooth();

  String[] initialCoordinates = jonny-
Track[0].split(",");
  lastLongitude =
float(initialCoordinates[0]);
  lastLatitude =
float(initialCoordinates[1]);

  println("1:" + " " + lastLongitude);
  println("1:" + " " + lastLatitude);

  String[] jonny_parts =  jonnyTrack[0].
split("7");
  jonnyWaypoints = new float[jonny_parts.
length][3];

  for (int i = 0; i < jonny_parts.length;
i++) {
    String[] coordinate_parts = jonny_
parts[i].split(",");

    float longitude = float(coordinate_
parts[0]);
    float latitude = float(coordinate_
parts[1]);

    if(longitude > maxLongitude) maxLongi-
tude = longitude;
    if(latitude > maxLatitude) maxLatitude
= latitude;
    if(longitude < minLongitude) minLongi-
tude = longitude;
    if(latitude < minLatitude) minLatitude
= latitude;

    waypointDistance = dist(longitude, lati-
tude, lastLongitude, lastLatitude);

    if(waypointDistance > maxWaypointDis-
tance) maxWaypointDistance = waypointDis-
tance;

    lastLongitude = longitude;
    lastLatitude = latitude;
```

Ashley Howell, Romana Egartner \\ JonnyPrint

```
float x = 0;
float y = 300;
float z = 200;
float step = 2;
float step2 = 1.5;

void setup() {
size(1000,500);
//background(0);
}

void draw() {
background(0);
fill(255,255,0);
ellipse(x, 250, 100, 100);
smooth();
fill(0);
ellipse(x+15, 220, 20,
20);
smooth();

triangle(x, 250, x+80,
y-50, x+80, z+50);
smooth();
x += step;
y -= step2;
z += step2;

if (z > 250) {
z = 200;
}
if (y < 250) {
y = 300;
}
if (x > 1050) {
x = -50;
}
//saveFrame();
```

Alin Cirstea \\ Packman_guru

```
package mikey;
import processing.core.*;
import processing.opengl.*;

@SuppressWarnings("serial")
public class mikey extends PApplet {

        final int WIDTH = 1920;
        final int HEIGHT = 1080;
        final float DISPLAY_SCALE = 0.5f;
        final int FRAMERATE = 30;
        final int DURATION = 60; // duration in seconds

        public void setup() {
                size((int)(WIDTH*DISPLAY_SCALE),
                -(int)(HEIGHT*DISPLAY_SCALE),
                -OPENGL);
                frameRate(FRAMERATE);
        }

        public void draw() {
                scale(DISPLAY_SCALE);
                background(0);
                float percent_done = (float)frame
                -Count/FRAMERATE/DURATION;
                stroke(100);
                fill(255);
                drawPoint(percent_done, 15);
        }

public static void main(String[] args) {
PApplet.main(new String[] { "mikey.mikey" });
}

//float pointsize = 100;
void drawPoint(float param, float size) {
                float x = param*WIDTH;
                line(0, HEIGHT/2, x, HEIGHT/2);
                ellipse(x, HEIGHT/2, size, size);
}
        }
```

Martin Gröbl \\ Mikey! Mikey!

Official Spam (A statistical Mimicry of the Art & Science Curriculum) by Martin Groedl was conceived at the time of an open letter, which was composed by all students and addressed to the heads of the study programme, leading to discussions about the curriculum within the Study Commission. The work is based on word counts and word combinations in the text of the curriculum. Based on this analysis an alternative text was generated, bearing similar statistical properties as the original but lacking any semantic coherence. By removing the connections that tie single words into a meaningful whole, the new text highlights the essence and vision of the programme, as communicated on the superficial level of words. Similar techniques are used in the creation of e-mail spam to automatically generate large amounts of natural-looking text.

From: "Dr. Gerald Bast" <gerald.bast@uni-ak.ac.at>, "Virgil Widrich" <virgil.widrich@uni-ak.ac.at>, "Alfred Vendl" <alfred.vendl@uni-ak.ac.at>, "Georg Glaeser" <georg.glaeser@uni-ak.ac.at>
Date: 24. Februar 2011 16:26:24 MEZ
To: Martin Leopold Grödl <groedl@gmx.net>
Subject: Re: Curriculum Art & Science Visualization

Welcome to the Angewandte!

The Art & Science Visualization Interdisciplinary Theory Seminar for Apparative Techniques of a scientific field of art. Current and developmental processes with Registration for experiments and science. The supervisors takes place through the end of the programme coordinator and methods for study law pursuant to apply visualisation strategies. Normally, the realisation of project work on enabling independent work and science and science, the planning of direct human perception become visible light (infrared, ultraviolet, microwaves, etc.) with their master thesis. The objective of utopia – with in the software systems required for study programme – is authorised by a comprehensive discussion on new media for exploring micro-art and their prior scientific/artistic knowledge transfer and the students through digital art, and problems.

The entrance examination commission has Academic degree For the project concept and Admission to project supervisors. The programme graduation ends with a letter of the content and nanoworlds. Biotechnology, imaging techniques still widely unused media artists, media history, among other hand, it is conducted collectively by a right of Science Visualization Interdisciplinary Project Work. This curriculum entered into question and in all of project work. Students can be appointed as a second wave had causal influence on individual interdisciplinary project work.

The programme is founded in the 1960s a comprehensive discussion on individual contribution of contact, and stimulate independent work prepared by means of temporal and exercise. The programme coordinator make use of knowledge and the Angewandte, whose founding mission advocates social development of art on the creative ability to link this significantly affected the next generation of project supervisors. The assignment of a public presentation of artistically applied "media" can be completed successfully. The main contents, Applied Media Design, for further work on coherent topics and methods for experiments and science; the registration for students are supervised as well as a general overview and in order to § 19, para. 1, no. 2.

Applied Representation Techniques of the field make use of projects and transdisciplinary approach and artistic production processes beyond the content comprised of the purpose of three phases. Art & Science Visualization Cultures Transdisciplinarity and photography, and Representation Techniques of the artistic/scientific exploration of electronic music, video art, as artistic production processes beyond the University professors of "Art & Science".

Rector Dr. Gerald Bast

Official Spam (A statistical Mimicry of the Art & Science Curriculum), 2011

Juliana Herrero, Acoustic Cloud Remix
For the annual art fair the Art & Science class tackled the construction of a stand that represented the University of Applied Arts.

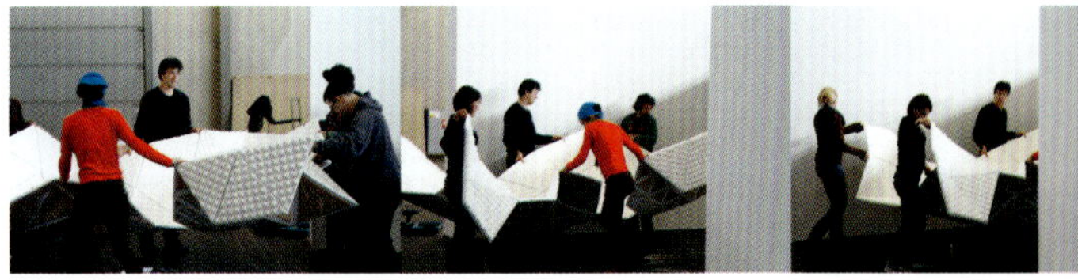

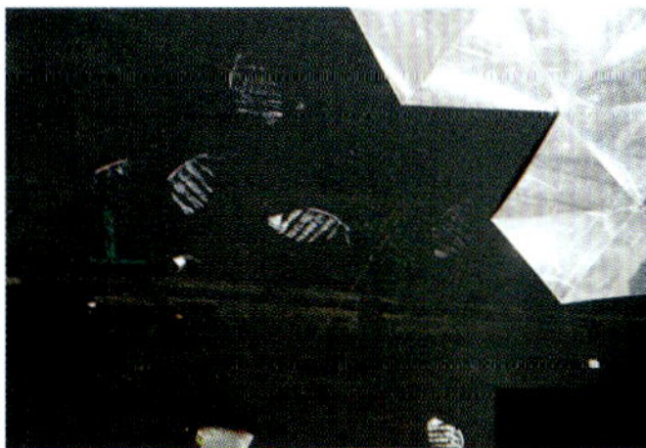

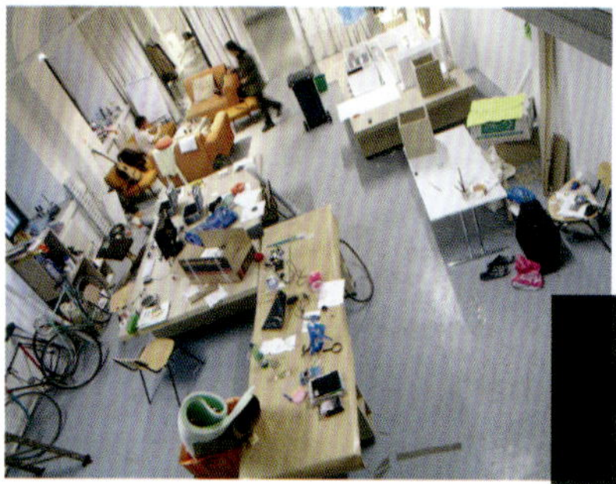

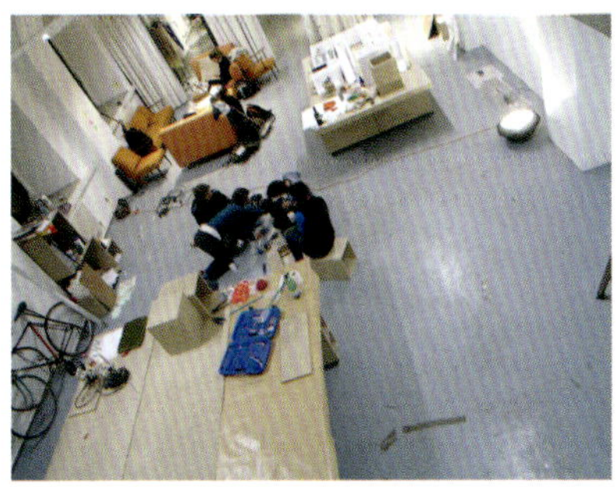

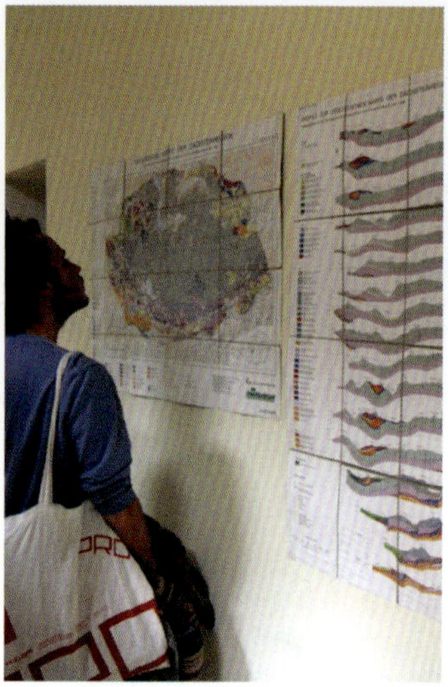

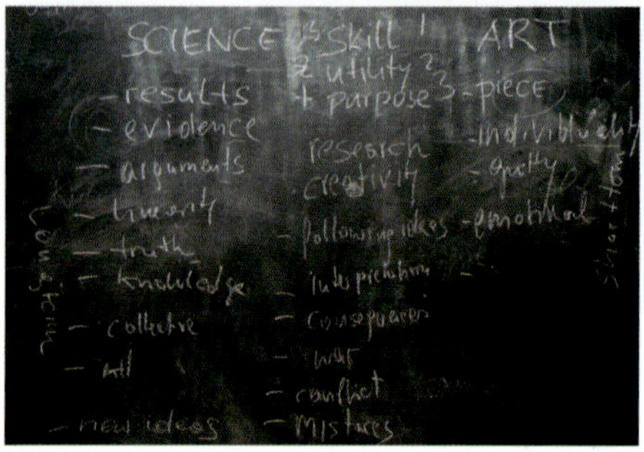
SCIENCE
skill
ART
utility
purpose
piece
- results
- evidence
- arguments
research
creativity
- truth
- emotional
- knowledge
- collective
- consequences
- war
- conflict
- new ideas
- mistakes

BIO:FICTION

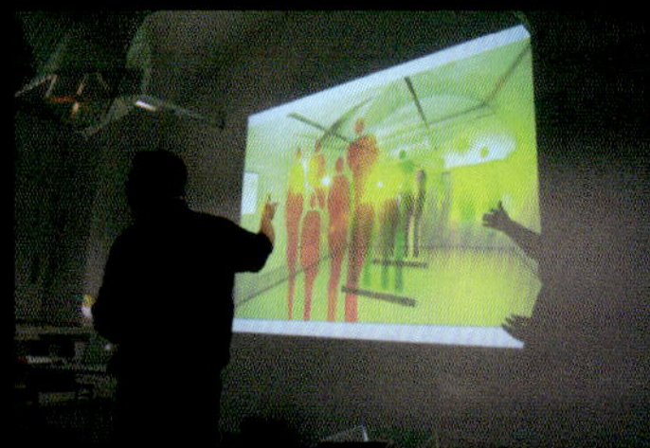

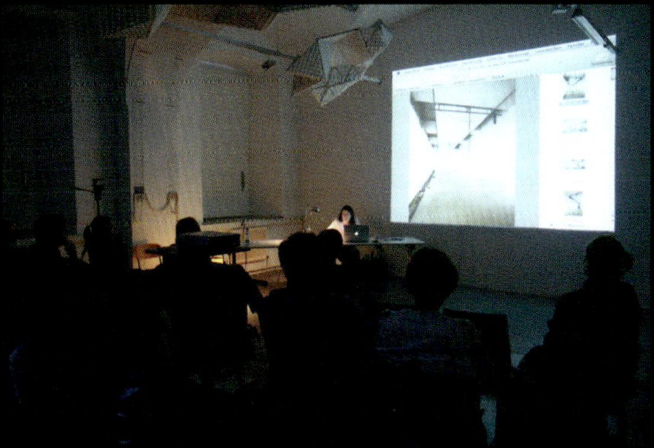

Kraeftner, B., et al

Penser avec ~~(la chemise de)~~ Marcel

A “shirt multiple” and a few notes on a “politique poïétique”

May 13th, 2011

Dear Marcel[1],

Here we are now - looking at the title of a work that you created 40 years ago. This title is in the form of a question. Can you remember it? Maybe we should trigger a short moment of reflection on what you were doing at that time. Unfortunately, we cannot ask you face to face, thus we have to rely on accounts of others. We are told that in the beginning of the 70s you took part in an advertising campaign for van Laack, a manufacturer of luxury shirts. And that your ad was placed in the German news magazine *Der Spiegel*. It is said that this work expresses one of your central subjects that deals with the corruption inherent to our Western consumer society, in which any authenticity is impossible. And that the ad can be read as a remedy provided by you, Marcel, to protect us - the reader of a news magazine - from the temptations of such a world.

Let us throw a brief glance at the online archive of *Der Spiegel*. There, in the issue 13/1971, we can find you, dear Marcel, or better the advert, surrounded by an article that reviews a book written by Norman Mailer with the title *Of a Fire on the Moon*.[2] It - the article - reflects the genre of "new journalism" and the relation of fiction and non-fiction writing. Interesting: You, the artist Marcel, the bad conscience of our capitalist (art) world, in the midst

-

(1) We are thinking with Marcel Broodthaers. Furthermore, we would like to frame the notion of "penser" by jumping on the shoulders of another giant: "*Penser, c'est experimenter, non pas interpreter, mais experimenter, et l'experimentation, c'est toujours l'actuel, le nouveau, ce qui est en train de se faire.*" In: Gilles Deleuze, *Pourparlers* (Paris: Editions Minuit, 1990), 144.
(2) Norman Mailer, *Of a Fire on the Moon*, (Boston: Little Brown & Co, 1970).

of a critical commentary that asks whether he, the artist Norman, is capable of giving back "to one of the most haunting scientific and technological endeavours of our history, the moon landing, its magic, its psyche, and its relation to the spirits of the underworld", as the author paraphrases the artist Norman.[3]

Marcel, were you aware of this fact? Was it your wish to appear in juxtaposition to Norman (a man of doubtful reputation, at least for many feminists)? Your critique of the role of mass media and advertising in juxtaposition to science and technology - as seen by an artist? Was the placement of the ad under your control? We don't know. Maybe it was not important to you at that time. In any case, the ad was placed in the culture and not in the business section of the magazine.

In the literature, this ad work, your appearance as a shirt model, was referred to as "*Publicité Chemise van Laack*". But stop! Which question are we referring to? When looking at the advert we cannot find any question. What we see is a photograph of a white, middle-aged man, looking at us, self-confident, a cigar in the left corner of his closed mouth. Yes, this man in front of a black background is you, Marcel, head-on, in a chequered shirt - *une chemise* - your hands making a dynamic gesture. The caption reads: "The director of the Musee d'Art Moderne, Department des Aigles, refused to wear the van Laack monocle."[4]

By the way, Marcel, did you give the naive *Spiegel* reader of 1971 the chance to enjoy your work? We are not referring to those people who visited, for example, "documenta 5" one year later and who,

-

(3) Author's translation: Hermann Schreiber, 'Der Teufel am Steuer?', *Der Spiegel*, 13 (1971), 164-166.

(4) The van Laack monocle refers to the distinctive look of the shirt buttons that have three holes (see later). Beneath the caption we can see a prominent van Laack logo and the ad text. It praises the properties of the shirt like materiality, aesthetics, exclusiveness, and functionality as rational criteria that justify an extraordinary price: "van Laack shirts are available at a price between 38 and 118 German Marks."

maybe, were able to catch the meaning of your intervention. We are referring to a reader who, being semi-educated in the arts, simply overlooked the distinctiveness of the ad during her or his reading of the Norman Mailer review. Was there any resolution in the magazine that solved the conundrum? We daresay that this was not the case. Probably, for you, Marcel, the work was not yet finished since it still lacked the varnish that transformed your work into an art piece. This transformation - this varnishing - must have taken place sometime after you had made a copy of the advert for your archive. It is this copy - with the varnish on it - that circulates nowadays in the art world. And it is this varnish in the form of a question that attracts our interest - and maybe it also would have attracted the attention of Norman. The handwritten question on the ad reads: *Que faut-il penser des rapports qui lient l'art, la publicité et le commerce? MB (le directeur)*.
Today, it is this question that lends the artwork its title: *What should we think about the relations that link art, advertising and commerce? MB (the director of the Musee d'Art Moderne, Department des Aigles)*.

But wait a minute. Why have you chosen to wear a shirt to formulate this question? Did you do it because shirts are part of the world of fashion and that this world is emblematic for a kind of superficial appearance? Could we speculate that you detested a world where the virtual or fictional replaced the real and where the borders between these two areas increasingly blurred? Where reality started to imitate fiction and, because for you - maybe - fiction equalled non-reality, you deduced that reality became unreal? Hence, that we are on the verge of a new and problematic reality of virtuality that is paradoxical and wrong?[5]
But maybe *we* are completely wrong and the case was much simpler and trivial: You put on this chequered shirt because you loved quality-made shirts, especially van Laack shirts, and your love came along

-

(5) Paraphrase of Esposito's commentary on Baudrillard in: Elena Esposito, *Die Fiktion der wahrscheinlichen Realität* (Frankfurt am Main: Suhrkamp Verlag, 2007).

with an awareness that, in the name of quality, advertising and commerce frequently create an aura that makes the real reality of production disappear. And that you liked to play with your and our ambivalence to taking part in the fashion game because you realised that this is a paradoxical game - a kind of a mutual imitation that attempts to implement one's own individuality and originality, i.e., striving for originality by doing what others do.[6][7]

By the way, dear Shirt-of-Marcel, do we find shirts of your kind when we explore the website of van Laack today? Of course not, since the stable world of instability, the trends of fashion, imply the change of your design, form, and price - but at least we find shirts that resemble you. In one of the shirt categories - "seasonal", "classic", "business", and "family affairs" - we find an example that shows a remote resemblance to you, Shirt-of-Marcel: It is called REDA F5TFC with a spread collar, semi-fitted, smooth button facing, no front pocket, for the price of € 149.90. Dear reader: You can find it here.[8]

Whereas you, Marcel, are wearing a shirt that should question the relations between art, advertising, and commerce, your colleague Norman (or better, his alter ego called "Aquarius") has entered *the* cathedral of science and technology and started to ponder a different question. But let's first give Norman the word:

> So, it was probably the Vehicle Assembly Building, which encouraged Aquarius to release the string of the balloon and let his ego float off to whatever would receive it. It was not that he suddenly decided to adopt the Space Program, or even approve it in part, it was just that he came to

-

(6) See: Elena Esposito, *Die Verbindlichkeit des Vorübergehenden: Paradoxien der Mode* (Frankfurt am Main: Suhrkamp Verlag, 2004).
(7) Today, forty years later, we learned to question or at least to distrust this special status of real reality and the condemnation of a fictional reality, and to assign a functional role in our society to this doubling of reality.
(8) www.vanlaack.de and search "REDA F5TFC".

> recognize that whatever was in store, a Leviathan was most certainly ready to ascend the heavens - whether for good or ill he might never know - but he was standing at least in the first cathedral of the age of technology, and he might as well recognize that the world would change, that the world *had* changed, even as he had thought to be pushing and shoving on it with *his* mighty ego. And it had changed in ways he did not recognize, had never anticipated, and could possibly not comprehend now. The change was mightier than he had counted on, the full brawn of the rocket in this cavernous womb of an immensity, this giant cathedral and bridge and box of a machine to put together a machine which would voyage through space, yes, this emergence of a ship to travel the ether, thrust across a vacuum, was no event he could measure by any philosophy he had yet put together in his brain.[9]

Norman gives the impression of someone who is overwhelmed. He is talking about his visit - probably wearing a white lab coat and a visitor's badge - to the Vehicle Assembly Building (VAB). He describes the VAB as a machine that assembles another machine: a huge carrier rocket called Saturn V. During his exploration of Cape Kennedy (now: Cape Canaveral), some days before the launch of the spacecraft called Apollo 11 his psyche and mind truly seem to be shocked by the fact that the world had changed without him being part of this change. The artist Norman seems to have a hard time to accept that the (male) white Anglo-Saxon Protestants (WASPs) of the Midwest had conquered the moon while he, artist Norman, was living through exciting but exhausting times on the East Coast.

We assume that Marcel's question underwent an anticipatory transformation or versioning in Norman's mind, which we would like to paraphrase as the following:

(9) See: Norman Mailer, 'A Fire on the Moon. A Major Report', *Life*, (1969), 25-41.

> What should we think about the relations that link art, advertising, and ~~commerce~~ science & technology?

and/or

> What should we think about the relations that link art, the public ~~advertising~~, and science & technology?

and/or

> What should we think about the relations that link art, ~~advertising~~ and ~~commerce~~ science & technology?

These versions of the question interest us. For us, these reformulations neither oppose nor replace Marcel's question, rather they extend, connect, and speak to it. When referring to science(s) and art(s), frequently differences and similarities play an important role. For instance, how do science(s) and art(s) relate to questions and answers? Some examples: Science is a question-driven endeavour ("questioning Nature"). Art gives answers without being interested in questions. Science gives answers to questions that have never been asked before. Art asks questions without being interested in answers, etc. Questioning and answering is framing our world, and this comes along, mostly, with someone who is asking or answering. This means, starting with Marcel and continuing with Norman, finally, we arrive at ourselves: We are posing the question about relationships of entities that seemingly already exist. And then, what about art(s) *and* science(s)? Some try to escape this dichotomising work between art(s) and science(s) by using expressions like "research", "artistic research", or "research-based art". Ultimately, we should perhaps stop asking and come back to the mundane world of everyday practices: what seem to be at stake are methods that are used in practice: "Tell me what method you use and I will tell you who you are."

This, dear Marcel, also holds true for ourselves - for those who are writing this article. At this point of writing, we are not sure whether we will be successful in escaping this boundary work[10] since we are constantly referring to those big categories called “Art” and “Science”. However, our method, used in this article, is to think with Marcel (and others), to reuse their work, to appropriate, re-purpose, enjoy, and reflect it in order to understand our own attitudes, prejudices, and thought concepts, which relate to a “scientificated” world.

In addition, as part of our method, we attempt to draw a rough sketch of a gallery of portraits, an assembly of versions of Marcel’s shirt (Norman, did you also wear chequered shirts from time to time?), which may create a more or less inspired background of references that come along with Marcel’s question and its versions. →

-

(10) Thomas F. Gieryn, ‘Boundary-Work and the Demarcation of Science from Non-Science: Strains and Interests in Professional Ideologies of Scientists’, *American Sociological Review*, 48 (1983), 781-795.

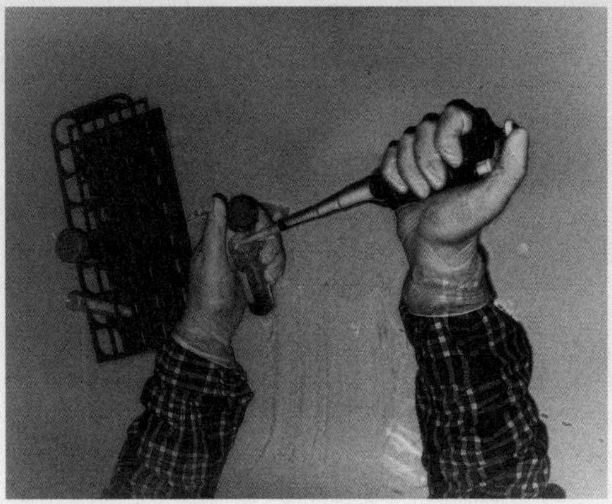

Mind the gap... and the unmarked space

-

"'Just like that, the strangest things happen just like that, you should know it by now...'
Like that, the shirt was found in Brussels. Its front, yesterday's Spiegel. Its torn off back, a window, and the reflecting mirror, today's."

The Empiricist's Shirt
A Foreign Body Sensation

-

"When he asked her if the foreign body sensation was still present, she replied, "If only it was!" and explained that the real problem was that she forgot about it all too often. Although it had cost a huge amount of money, it was very obvious that the desired effect had not set in yet. He hung up with the advice to be patient because these things would take some time and returned to preparing his morning coffee."

<u>she does not wear plaid</u>

-

"Que ce qu'on fait quand on n'en peut
plus, si on est rassasié.
Jouer?
La nourriture devient vêtement /
costume. Rester á l'éxterieure."

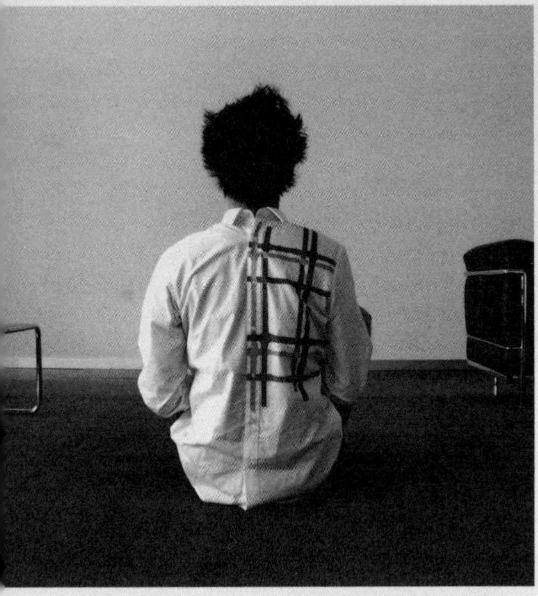

<u>modernity facing the future</u>

-

"Shirt: H&M (Mariahilferstrasse
78-80 / 12.05.2011 19:06)
€14.95. 106 38 Stockholm, Sweden.
Made in Bangladesh
EUR M / US M / CA M / CN 175/100
machine wash warm, only non-chlorine
bleach when needed,
line dry, medium iron.
65% polyester 35% cotton
pattern drawn by hand"

<u>Drinking Coffee at IMBA*</u>

-

"When I left... a sentence came to my mind: 'When you do this type of conceptual work, every decision you make is very critical for the outcome of the work.'" (*IMBA: Institute for Molecular Biotechnology of the Austrian Academy of Sciences)

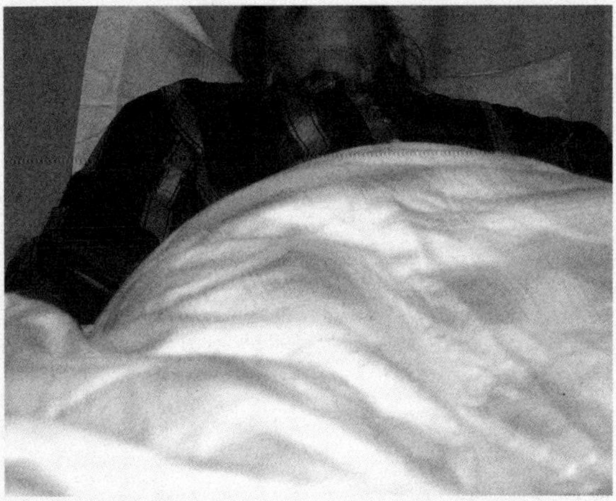

Embedding, 2011

-

"If I embed the shirt in different processes, methods, techniques, traces, or whatsoever, a broad horizon emerges before me. I can even think of my shirt in the future because its embeddedness in all of these processes gives me freedom. Freedom to think, to act, to make decisions, reflect. It is also a subtle gesture, a certain sensibility, sensitivity, a respect for this non-human being, to bed it on a pillow and tuck it in. We live in an uncertain world, and tonight, perhaps, I will lift the shirt out of the bed and into the world, into uncertainty."

dramatising disciplinary rule enforcement

-

"Of course, you are the artist, scientist, whatever. But don't let that limit your engagement in providing valuable ideas for your interdisciplinary project to your own field! Often the key ideas for certain problems cannot be linked to isolated disciplinary frameworks. Good, successful interdisciplinary work is characterised by 'hybrid' ideas - kind of like when an artist poses a good research question or a scientist makes a statement beside that what is given. Real interdisciplinary collaboration is priceless."

wearing **BRAIN** *shirts* *is so HOT!*

PREZERVE GOOD IDEAS

<u>skyrtu-verkefni, 2011</u>

-

"the world has no problem because I am sleeping"

<u>lab-disposable</u>

-

"Westbury

100% cotton/coton/baumwolle/katoen/algodon/cotone/algodao"

Trust in images

-

"The artist_scientist refused to appear in the picture, however, he wears a monocle."

Der Spiegel, 22 März 2011

KULTUR

Der Produzent dieser Photographie weigerte sich termingerecht einzureichen.

Natürlich bekommen Sie für den Preis eines van Laack Hemdes zwei andere.

Nur sind das eben keine van Laack Hemden. Den seidenweichen und glatten Sitz des Kragens, den vollendeten Schnitt und die exklusiven Dessins finden Sie höchstens noch bei Maßhemden. Der Stoff ist reine unverfälschte Baumwolle. Ein Hemd, das sich sehr angenehm auf der Haut trägt und sich – tropfnaß aufgehängt – in 7 Minuten bügeln läßt. Ohne die Vorzüge reiner Baumwolle zu verlieren.

van Laack Hemden gibt es von DM 38,- bis DM 118,-

van Laack DAS KÖNIGLICHE HEMD

es den blühenden Blödsinn Mailerscher Traum-Theorien über den „Super-Vulkanismus" auf dem Mond, gibt es aber auch Beschreibungen des Mondes, wie sie kein Astronaut, der dort war, je formulieren kann.

Der Rezensent muß freilich zugeben, daß er nicht ganz unparteiisch ist. Auch er hat über Apollo 11 zu berichten gehabt, und er wird ganz grün vor Neid, wenn er jetzt bei Mailer liest, was er alles nicht gesehen, nicht gerochen, nicht einmal geahnt, geschweige denn geschrieben hat. Aber er treibt sich, anders als Mailer, bereits seit den frühen Gemini-Flügen gelegentlich im Ambiente der bemannten Weltraumfahrt herum und wagt deshalb die Behauptung, daß dieses Ambiente noch nicht treffender geschildert worden ist als in Mailers Buch; daß die Nasa von ihren Anfängen „in einer Landschaft der politischen Ränke, des wirtschaftlichen Zynismus, der Zauberei und der Manöver von Lyndon Johnsons Fettlebe-Brigade" bis zu ihrer Vertreibung aus dem Paradies der nationalen Prioritäten noch nie einem besseren Reporter in die Hände gefallen ist als dem Wassermann Mailer.

Hier ist einer unter die Journalisten gegangen (und man weiß dies natürlich schon seit „Heere aus der Nacht"), der seinen Zunftgenossen nicht bloß den Atem und die Sprachkraft des Romanciers voraus hat, sondern auch die ungenierte Einsicht des „eigenen Überflüssigwerdens" angesichts einer immer komplexeren, immer schwerer zu beschreibenden Wirklichkeit.

Aber Norman Mailer versucht nicht, sich diesem Dilemma dadurch zu entziehen, daß er die komplexe Wirklichkeit mißt und sortiert anhand der Normen eines Systems, um ihrer so Herr werden zu können. Er schreibt einfach gegen sein Dilemma an, wütend, wortgewaltig, aber auch verzagt, verzweifelt — und er gewinnt.

Wenn es wahr ist (und ich fürchte, es ist wahr), daß Journalisten immer zuerst für Journalisten schreiben, dann sollte dem Gewerbe die pädagogische Potenz dieses Buches nicht verlorengehen. Dann sollte man es in den Verbandsblättern unter „Bücher für Kollegen" anzeigen, damit wir Kollegen wieder mal merken, wie schlecht es der Reportage hierzulande geht und wie mausetot in Wahrheit das sogenannte Feature ist: ein ausgebleichtes Derivat der angelsächsischen Color-Story, gleich weit entfernt von objektiver Information wie von subjektiver Impression, abgesoffen in den brackigen Fluten des Journalesischen, das nicht Deutsch ist und auch sonst nicht viel.

Solche Kollegen jedenfalls, für die Journalismus noch etwas anderes ist als ein kollektiv zu betreibendes Vehikel der Systemüberwindung, können bei Norman Mailer (weiß Gott keinem „Rechten") lernen, was Reportage sein könnte, wenn bei uns die Reporter mehr mit Literatur und die Literaten mehr mit Reportage im Sinn hätten.

Wenn nämlich beides — wie hier — zusammengeht, dann herzlichen Glückwunsch dem Leser.

166 que faut-il penser des rapports qui lient la science, la publicité, l'art (et le commerce)? WS (le créateur)

inter sanguinem, faecem et urinam nascimur ?!?

1971, Werbeanzeige für van Laack, in: Der Spiegel, 22. März 1971, S. 166

61

-

"ch-ch-changes - turn and face the head*
Lyrics D.Bowie"

Bloodwork

-

"Inter sanguinem, faecem et urinam nascimur?!?"

<u>light harvesting shirt</u>

-

"shirt and me and context becoming blurred"

<u>Laboratory camouflage</u>

-

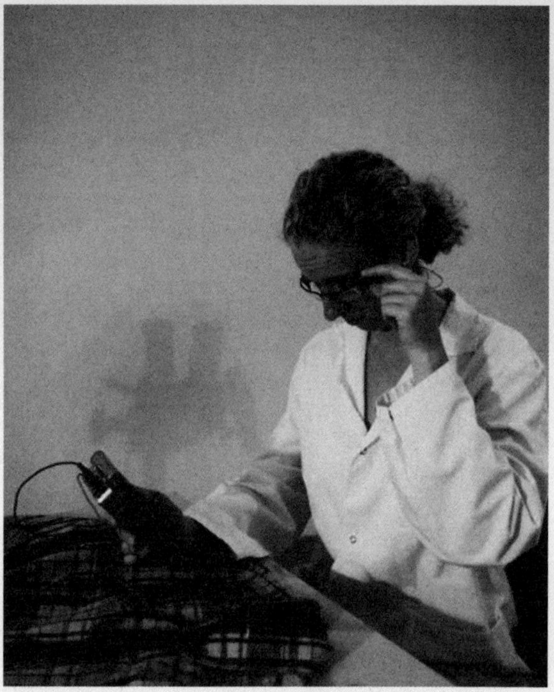

Auratic → ☼

-

"The shirt is one of my most favourites, but actually in unknown state and unknown place. As I was trying to make it nicer, I destroyed it - too much heat on the screen print dryer. so... resemblance... focus just on the label... ☼ is enough for me."

The Positivist's Shirt

-

"It's the shirt that matters."

Interpellation
-
“Shirt from Caritas, Vienna,
4th district”

self-made shirt
-
“disguising, revealing, representing”

Figure 3: The boy wears the shirt

-

"The pivot point in the art and science relationship is of description and prescription. If we say they are separate then we may refer to them as both; so said, both operate simultaneously in both modes (insert points at will here). Feeding up and feeding down, filtering up and filtering down, if you will."

Participatory observation

-

"What should we think of the relation between art, public and science"

Horror Vacui

-

"Que faut-il penser d'une publicité sans produit?"

→ What kind of method did you, Marcel, apply during your short artist life? We are told that you were adhering to a "politique magique", which you pursued by changing between roles, media, worlds, and languages; that this "politique" was to disarrange our common sense of signification and that, consequently, you had to implant yourself in the so-called in-between.[11]

-

(11) Sabine Folie and Gabriele Mackert (eds.), *Marcel Broodthaers - Politique Poetique*. Kunsthalle Wien, 02.07.03-26.10.03 (Vienna: Kunsthalle Wien, 2003).

Marcel, did you spend some time at van Laack? Did you have a look at the capitalists, the production facilities, the workers? Did you wander through the repositories of fine cloth and yarns? Did you take part in the art, the practice, and the politics of shirt crafting? The shirt you were wearing - was it your creation? And did it - becoming a Marcel-with-a-van-Laack-shirt - change your life? Unfortunately, we don't know. But in case you did so, we think, today, we would appreciate your attempt to take part in a kind of "Dingpolitik"(12) that tries to bypass an attitude of critique(13) - an (experimental) art with a sense of humour that is perplexed by the results of its own practices.(14) Could it be, though, that you would have objected - like many artists do - to the use of the term "method" in the context of arts: Would you have rejected the idea of an (experimental) art that might apply (restrictive?) experimental methods rather than relying exclusively on (free-floating?) creativity, inspiration, or infantine play?

> So Aquarius began to live without his ego, a modest quiet observer who went on trips through the Space Centre and took in interviews, and read pieces of literature connected to the subject, and spent lonely nights not drinking in his air-conditioned motel room, and thought - not of himself but the size of the feat and the project before him, and by the night before the launch he was already in orbit himself, a simple fellow with a mind which idled agreeably, his mind indeed out in some weightless trip through the vacuum of a psychic space, for a mind without ego he was discovering is akin to a body without gravity.(15)

-

(12) See, e.g.: Bruno Latour and Peter Weibel (eds.), *Making Things Public: Atmospheres of Democracy* (Cambridge, MA/Karlsruhe: MIT Press & ZKM/Center for Art and Media Karlsruhe, 2005).
(13) Bruno Latour, 'Why Has Critique Run Out of Steam? From Matters of Fact to Matters of Concern', *Critical Inquiry*, 30 (2004), 225.
(14) On the difference of irony and humour, see: Isabelle Stengers, *Die Erfindung der modernen Wissenschaften* (Frankfurt am Main: Campus Verlag, 1997), 104.
(15) Norman Mailer, 'A Fire on the Moon. A Major Report', 30.

Norman generously allows us a brief glimpse into his toolbox. From a repertoire of methods[16] that relate to journalistic investigations and/or social science research methods he creates a "new journalism"[17] patchwork of formats, where he combines the colour story, the expert interview, a first-person report of some kind, the backgrounder, and the analysis (to name only a few) in order to write a report about the moon landing and NASA. Interestingly, by talking about his ego and alcohol abstinence, he insinuates that these ingredients should not be part of any scientific research method: they are methods that need a sober collective of architects of knowledge (presumably in white lab coats).

It was no secret that the artist Norman got a tremendous honorarium from *LIFE* to write this "major report".[18] Maybe there were additional cheques from other sources. Norman worked for money and involved himself in the business of science communication. In his report, he described facts and figures about a politically highly sensitive endeavour. However, it is not coarse advertising or propaganda for science and technology. By using his novelist capabilities he rather points to the unabashed insight of his own dispensability in an increasingly complex reality. And it is this reality that, for him, is increasingly difficult to describe - a fact that produces a dilemma for Norman. However, his representation does not attempt to circumvent this dilemma by applying the measuring and ordering norms of the system that he aims to describe, rather, "he writes in order to attack this dilemma - angry, powerfully eloquent, and at the same time disheartened and in desperation".[19]

-

(16) David Randall, *The Universal Journalist* (London: Pluto Press, 2007), 213-217. The author provides an extensive list of methods for writing a feature, for instance: colour story, fly on the wall, behind the scenes, in disguise, profile, interview, fact boxes, chronology, a history of…, full texts, my testimony, backgrounder, analysis, vox pops, experts' round up, opinion poll, review, extended reporting.

(17) Another famous representative of this journalistic genre that emerged in the 60s is Gay Talese, who became famous for longstanding and meticulous investigations of his subjects.

(18) A note for clarification: The book review in the *Der Spiegel* refers to the German translation of the book *Of a Fire on the Moon*, which was published after Mailer had written his serialised report for *LIFE*.

(19) Hermann Schreiber, 'Der Teufel am Steuer?', *Der Spiegel*, 1971, 164-166.

> "What should we think about the relations that link art, advertising, and ~~commerce~~ science & technology?"

We think that Norman did not apply Marcel's method of a "politique magique" in order to counterbalance a reality that he, Norman, might have considered as being non-authentic. However, by mixing fragments of fiction with realistic accounts he, maybe, would have shared with Marcel the idea that the only way to come close to reality is by evoking a fictional reality: a reality of "poetique" that explores the reality of "politique". Here it is again: the split between fictitious reality and real reality. How shall we relate to this split of reality? Maybe this split does not exist, or, it is not important.

In this text, up to now, we were wearing shirts. However, what would happen if, instead of shirts, all of us - at least temporarily - would wear skirts? Maybe the cleavage would disappear and we would start to mix realities.
Up to now, we referred to white, shirt wearing, male witnesses of science and technology. Maybe we should hand over the word to another (modest) witness of technoscience - this time a female one: Donna Haraway. Although Donna also wears shirts[20] she comments on Marcel's and Norman's questions in a different way that seems to avoid the aforementioned dichotomy. In her writings, she embraces the heterogeneity of a patchwork reality of technoculture and envisages a politicophilosophical programme that we would like to call a "politique poïétique".
When leafing through the pages of one of Donna's books[21] we stumble across a few images: We see a female cyborg sitting at a table with her hands on a keyboard. Furthermore, in the form of a diagrammatic

-

(20) Nowadays, by means of a quick online image search, it is easy to gain a superficial glance on the way people dress themselves in public.
(21) Donna J. Haraway, *Simians, Cyborgs, and Women: The Reinvention of Nature* (New York: Routledge, 1990).

cartoon ("the immunological orchestra"), we see the evolution of the theoretical framework for the functioning of the immune system: there is the image of an AIDS memorial quilt of the *Names Project*; the advert of a company that manufactures products for dealing with animal cell cultures; another ad for a DNA sequencing system; and a tableau of some macroscopic body images from a coffee table book by Lennart Nilsson.

> "What should we think about the relations that link ~~art~~, advertising, commerce, and science & technology?"

By presenting this imagery Donna points to a struggle at a new last frontier. Some years after Normans report about the moon landing, science, and in particular (micro)biology, has declared a mission that heads for another celestial body, located infinitely remote and at the same time infinitely close by: It is the mission to cultivate our human bodies, the colonisation of an unknown and wild territory, the promised land of wealth and health. Donna associates this endeavour of technoscience with the mentality of settler societies who have developed a specific attitude towards the role of time. These societies face the future with a "teleological, goal-directed orientation", where "the present is nothing but a vanishing point of transition toward what is to come, whether that be destruction or redemption".[22]
And then she hands over the word to an artist colleague of Marcel and Norman, to Patricia[23], who, in her work, comments on the unintentional consequences of these transition phases: "In my work, perhaps I am saying that whether you like them or you don't like them, we actually have a duty to care. We created them, so we've got to look after them."[24] Patricia refers to imperfect, messy,

-

(22) Donna J. Haraway, 'Speculative Fabulations for Technoculture's Generations', in *(tender) Creature Exhibition Catalogue* (2007), 1-9 <http://www.patriciapiccinini.net>, accessed 14 July 2011.
(23) We are referring to Patricia Piccinini.
(24) Ibid.

collateral realities - which she prefers to call "critters" - that are frequently produced by science and technology. Dear Donna and Patricia, does this mean that we have to develop a kind of logic of care, a "responsive attentiveness"[25] not only for our successful accomplishments but also for our failures and errors, our by-products of progress, the collateral damages, misuses, maximum credible accidents? Do we have to develop a sense of responsibility for these "critters of technoculture" - be they "natural or not, good or not, safe or not"?[26] And that we have to learn a new way of knowing that you, Donna, call "situational knowledges" where "actors come in many and wonderful forms? Accounts of a 'real' world do not, then, depend on a logic of 'discovery', but on a power-charged social relation of 'conversation'. The world neither speaks itself nor disappears in favour of a master decoder."[27]

What is more, she - Donna - considers it as worthwhile to flavour her political manoeuvre with a pinch of humour: "Such a sense of humour is not comfortable for humanists and others committed to the world as resource. Richly evocative figures exist for feminist visualizations of the world as witty agent. We need not lapse into an appeal to a primal mother resisting becoming resource. The Coyote or Trickster, embodied in American Southwest Indian accounts, suggest our situation when we give up mastery but keep searching for fidelity, knowing all the while we will be hoodwinked." And then Donna suggests that "these are useful myths for scientists who might be our allies. Feminist objectivity makes room for surprises and ironies at the heart of all knowledge production; we are not in charge of the world. We just live there and try to strike up non-innocent conversations by means of our prosthetic devices, including our visualization technologies. No wonder science fiction has been such

-

(25) Haraway borrows this term from Deborah Bird Rose's book, *Reports from a Wild Country: Ethics for Decolonisation* (Sydney: University of New South Wales Press, 2004).
(26) Donna J. Haraway, 'Speculative Fabulations for Technoculture's Generations'.
(27) Donna J. Haraway, *Simians, Cyborgs, and Women: The Reinvention of Nature*, 198.

a rich writing practice in recent feminist theory. I like to see feminist theory as a reinvented coyote discourse obligated to its enabling sources in many kinds of heterogeneous accounts of the world."[28]

Donna, did you know that a colleague of Marcel, Joseph, had started a three-day (non-innocent) conversation with a coyote in a New York art gallery back in 1974?[29] His prosthetic devices were a cane or shepherd's crook, a huge felt cape - not a van Laack shirt - a stack of issues of the *Wall Street Journal*, and turbine noise from a tape recorder. It is said that, finally, the coyote - his name was Little John - lost his distrust and started to use those devices in a way that he considered as appropriate (e.g. urinating on the *WSJ*, tearing the felt apart). Could the performance of Joseph and the coyote be considered as a lab experiment in comparative psychology, in which both Little John and Joseph hoodwinked each other and, maybe, learned how to "*penser*" with each other?

Marcel, we apologise... we know that your relationship to Joseph was not an easy one and that you thought that humour was more a part of your repertoire. However, at this point we would like to thank you, Marcel, that you gave us the opportunity to ponder about you, your shirt, and some questions that came to our minds when we were looking at your advert in *Der Spiegel* from the year 1971. It helped us to reflect on a "politique poïétique" that does not aim to play any real reality off against a fictional reality. A politics that implies, for us, dear Marcel, that we have to develop methods of taking care[30] of issues that emerge from our interest in matters of

-

(28) Ibid., 201.

(29) We are referring to a performance of Joseph Beuys called *I like America and America likes me*, Gallery René Block, New York, 1974.

(30) On the notion of "care", see, e.g.: Annemarie Mol, Ingunn Moser, and Jeannette Pols (eds.), *Care in Practice: On Tinkering in Clinics, Homes and Farms* (Bielefeld: Transcript, 2010).

concern[31] that we form part of. A politics that, hopefully, comes along with a different temporality that takes the present seriously and not doesn't just pass through it to elsewhere, as Donna puts it in her comment on Patricia's work, a present that maybe introduces the authenticity that you, Marcel, were dreaming of - 40 years ago.[32]

-

(31) By "matters of concern" we refer to issues that more or less directly affect our identity. A flavour for the role of science as a trigger for matters of concern, see, e.g.: Michel Callon, Pierre Lascoumes, and Yannick Barthe, *Acting in an Uncertain World: An Essay on Technical Democracy*, tr. Graham Burchell (Cambridge, MA: MIT Press, 2009).

(32) Of course, we also want to thank you, Norman, Donna, and Patricia, for helping us to think by means of your work(s).

Der Spiegel, 22 märz 1971 –

KULTUR

es den blühenden Blödsinn Mailerscher Traum-Theorien über den „Super-Vulkanismus" auf dem Mond, gibt es aber auch Beschreibungen des Mondes, wie sie kein Astronaut, der dort war, je formulieren kann.

Der Rezensent muß freilich zugeben, daß er nicht ganz unparteiisch ist. Auch er hat über Apollo 11 zu berichten gehabt, und er wird ganz grün vor Neid, wenn er jetzt bei Mailer liest, was er alles nicht gesehen, nicht gerochen, nicht einmal geahnt, geschweige denn geschrieben hat. Aber er treibt sich, anders als Mailer, bereits seit den frühen Gemini-Flügen gelegentlich im Ambiente der bemannten Weltraumfahrt herum und wagt deshalb die Behauptung, daß dieses Ambiente noch nicht treffender geschildert worden ist als in Mailers Buch; daß die Nasa von ihren Anfängen „in einer Landschaft der politischen Ränke, des wirtschaftlichen Zynismus, der Zauberei und der Manöver von Lyndon Johnsons Fettlebe-Brigade" bis zu ihrer Vertreibung aus dem Paradies der nationalen Prioritäten noch nie einem besseren Reporter in die Hände gefallen ist als dem Wassermann Mailer.

Hier ist einer unter die Journalisten gegangen (und man weiß dies natürlich schon seit „Heere aus der Nacht"), der seinen Zunftgenossen nicht bloß den Atem und die Sprachkraft des Romanciers voraus hat, sondern auch die ungenierte Einsicht des „eigenen Überflüssigwerdens" angesichts einer immer komplexeren, immer schwerer zu beschreibenden Wirklichkeit.

Aber Norman Mailer versucht nicht, sich diesem Dilemma dadurch zu entziehen, daß er die komplexe Wirklichkeit mißt und sortiert anhand der Normen eines Systems, um ihrer so Herr werden zu können. Er schreibt einfach gegen sein Dilemma an, wütend, wortgewaltig, aber auch verzagt, verzweifelt — und er gewinnt.

Wenn es wahr ist (und ich fürchte, es ist wahr), daß Journalisten immer zuerst für Journalisten schreiben, dann sollte dem Gewerbe die pädagogische Potenz dieses Buches nicht verlorengehen. Dann sollte man es in den Verbandsblättern unter „Bücher für Kollegen" anzeigen, damit wir Kollegen wieder mal merken, wie schlecht es der Reportage hierzulande geht und wie mausetot in Wahrheit das sogenannte Feature ist: ein ausgebleichtes Derivat der angelsächsischen Color-Story, gleich weit entfernt von objektiver Information wie von subjektiver Impression, abgesoffen in den brackigen Fluten des Journalesischen, das nicht Deutsch ist und auch sonst nicht viel.

Solche Kollegen jedenfalls, für die Journalismus noch etwas anderes ist als ein kollektiv zu betreibendes Vehikel der Systemüberwindung, können bei Norman Mailer (weiß Gott keinem „Rechten") lernen, was Reportage sein könnte, wenn bei uns die Reporter mehr mit Literatur und die Literaten mehr mit Reportage im Sinn hätten.

Wenn nämlich beides — wie hier — zusammengeht, dann herzlichen Glückwunsch dem Leser.

X Der Directeur du Musée d'Art Moderne, Departement des Aigles, weigerte sich, das van Laack Monokel zu tragen.

Natürlich bekommen Sie für den Preis eines van Laack Hemdes zwei andere.

Nur sind das eben keine van Laack Hemden. Den seidenweichen und glatten Sitz des Kragens, den vollendeten Schnitt und die exklusiven Dessins finden Sie höchstens noch bei Maßhemden. Der Stoff ist reine unverfälschte Baumwolle. Ein Hemd, das sich sehr angenehm auf der Haut trägt und sich – tropfnaß aufgehängt – in 7 Minuten bügeln läßt. Ohne die Vorzüge reiner Baumwolle zu verlieren.

van Laack
DAS KÖNIGLICHE HEMD

van Laack Hemden gibt es von DM 38.- bis DM 118.-

166

Que faut-il penser des rapports qui ~~[illegible]~~ lient l'art, la publicité et le commerce? M.B. (le directeur)

–

Que faut-il penser des rapports que lient l'art, la publicité et la commerce? M.B.(le directeur)-Publicité van Laack, Advertisement for van Laack, 1971 in: *Der Spiegel*, 22. March 1971, 166, Courtesy Estate Marcel Broodthaers, Brussels.

Kraeftner, B., et al

Penser avec ~~(la chemise de)~~ Marcel

A "shirt multiple" and a few notes on a "politique poïétique"

Johanna Schaffer

Artistic Re-re-research

Translated by Kevin Dooley

Tom: ...no one has yet been able to convince me that artistic research really is a sexy place...
Johanna: (laughs)
Tom: ...as much and as hard as I try to convince myself...

The above is taken from an interview with my colleague Tom Holert on the term "artistic research" and its discursive field, which I conducted for a research project that we are both involved in.[1] My text begins with this rather heretical remark because, coming from one of the protagonists of the institutional field of artistic research, I find it to be fairly unusual, and because I'd like to imagine that this unexpectedness is able to insert a moment of pause within otherwise busy processes of diligent construction and production.

Moreover, I sometimes share his point of view. And if I don't (and I am sure that Tom Holert himself often has a different opinion), it is at those times that I am intrigued by the ways in which this newly established discursive site is vibrating with charges of institutional power, promises of funding, individual desires, and fierce movements and rhetorics of legitimisation – a condensation of a lot of activity and a lot of passion. My contribution addresses artistic research as an institutional discourse that has been propelled by recent restructurings of academic art education in Austria, as well as in the EU more broadly, according to the dictates of the so-called Bologna process.[2] It will primarily present a couple of polemical remarks intended to stress dissensus rather than the pragmatic and instrumental consensus that seems to prevail in the field. The polemics emerged from experiences made within the following three institutional contexts of artistic research:

First, the Academy of Fine Arts Vienna's PhD in Practice programme that Tom Holert, Renate Lorenz, and I helped to set up and have run since October 2010.[3] Many people at the Academy were involved in building up the programme, and much of this work was car-

David Kellner, Still from the animation film "Rundgangfilm 2007", A 2007. (The film was also used in the recent work "who I am & what I hate", see http://1200m.org/soil.html)

ried out by unpaid students who engaged in that process because they found the possibility that emerged a promising one – the possibility, as an artist, to do a PhD. I am highlighting this background story because, on the level of micropolitics in the fields of concentrated institutional power, I consider the question of who can and actually does participate in the creation of structures to be decisive.

The second context was a discussion with the Berlin-based artist and PhD in Practice candidate at the Academy in Vienna, Michael Baers, which I requested after he told me that he was researching the European PhD in Practice programmes.[4] Here's Michael Baers:

> My last train of thought is about a kind of paternalism one can really identify in this artistic research debate, where these theorists or non-artists are putting forward a model that artists then have to oedipalize themselves in relation to.[5]

The third is the research project *Troubling Research. Performing Knowledge in the Arts*, a project in which nine artists and theorists (myself included) investigate the contemporary institutional conditions as well as historical and contemporary forms of practice within what can be referred to as artistic research.[6] The project is interested in the extension of critical (self) reflexivity in the field of artistic research and reserves a fair amount of scepticism towards the way this field, as it emerges in Austria and elsewhere, tends to promote a concept of research that is based on notions of linearity, unambiguousness, accountability, verifiability, and accumulation. This also applies to the way artistic research is represented by funding agencies and rectors and managers of arts universities.

Kathrin Busch refers to the conception of research as the basis of objective science as "anachronistic"[7] and as being surprisingly unmarked by any of the post-positivist or constructivist-based critiques of science that have emerged in recent decades. For *Troubling Research* it is then a case of thematising this re-actualisation of an anachronistic or, with Alex Demirović's domination-critical formulation, technical-instrumentalist concept of research in the field of fine art.[8] Moreover, the project aims to experiment with and popularise forms of knowledge production and figures of thinking that are attentive to the dimensions of the processual, to conditionalities, relationalities, ambivalences, dissents, and conflicts. In the interviews I have been conducting with the other eight project partners, I have asked them, amongst other things, if and how they find this concept of artistic research useful in their individual art and/or theory practices – if, for example, it makes it easier to access money or symbolic capital, or whether they find that it also has obstructive effects. (Most of the interview excerpts quoted in this text originated in this context.)

That's the context. Now the polemic, in three points:

The currently booming discourse on artistic research, as well as art and science, is in many ways ahistorical, in terms of both its object – artistic research – as well as in relation to itself. Differently said, this discourse often acts as if the practice of artistic research had only just been invented by the institutionally supported discourse on artistic research. Often enough, this discourse also appears to be largely unreflexive in relation to the institutional and political conditions of its coming into being, especially with regard to its foundation in the recent politics of education and knowledge (Bologna process!).

Secondly, the contemporary discourse on artistic research frequently rests on a substantialist and mythologising notion of art as well as artistic production. It is also based on notions of science and knowledge that are oriented towards accumulation and commodification, and feed on the myths of transparency and objectivity. A conservative notion of science is therefore coupled with a conservative notion of art, and the conservatism of this coupling might be less obvious because the genealogy of research-based art practices is generally narrated from a constructivist, critical, and left-wing standpoint.[9]

The third point, as formulated by the artist Michael Baers, is that the contemporary discourse on artistic research is in many ways paternalising in regard to artists. Furthermore, and perhaps not unrelated to this initial observation, one can discern that this discourse primarily leads to economic support for people who are in knowledge management and administrative positions, much more so than it finances artists.

I'm engaging in this polemic because it seems worthwhile to highlight the differing and conflictual positions that are currently emerging in the contemporary discourse of artistic research, and to recognise them as such – as different and conflictual. In this way, their potential for conflict can, for instance, be used in order to focus attention on how – in and through the discourse of artistic research – a state of discussion in the field of art has been displaced. It might even be more precise to talk about a kind of cutting, the production of an ellipsis or eclipse (the name rhetorics gives to figures of speech marked by a cutting away and leaving out). That which has been cut out and away is a state of discussion that, at least in contexts that saw themselves as politically inspired, was generated during the course of the 1980s and 90s through institutional critique, through feminist, anti-racist, anti-capitalist, and queer critiques. This state of discussion implied relying on an anti-essentialising, historical, and socially-based conception of art, as well as on critical epistemologies. Part of the work of critical epistemologies has been exactly its critique of traditional natural science dominated notions of knowledge and science with their fantasies of neutrality, transparency, and objectivity. Thus, the institutional field of artistic research is proving to be a catalyst for specific processes of theory transformation.

Furthermore, in the conversation I had with Michael Baers, he spoke of a specific transformation of the conception of art towards an, as he put it, "essentially positivist notion of art" that is based on the idea "that art can be improved and therefore is a mode of knowledge that is cumulative".[10] This positivist conception of art is combined, according to Baers, with a positivist natural science-based conception of science for the benefit of a specific project:

> I think that this [art's] comparison with science is actually motivated by particular economic considerations that have to do with the obliteration of the humanities in the research university – not in every context, but in America it is happening, also in the UK (think of the Middlesex philosophy department getting removed).[11]

Michael Baer's thesis is based on his observations of the discursive field of artistic research in the UK and the USA, and is not directly transferable onto the German-speaking or Austrian context. (Mika Hannula, another one of my interviewees, says that one's speech in this field is always characterised by a high amount of particularity.)[12] However, it is reminiscent of what Alex Demirović describes as a process of technocratic reform at German-speaking universities that has already been going on for over 40 years: the attempt to guarantee the dominance of a technical-instrumental notion of knowledge within educational policy.[13] However, he particularly emphasises that what is remarkable is not the persistence of this trend (of technocratic reform) but the fact that it hasn't been pushed through to the desired extent.

The most recent developments of the universities also form the immediate context of the emergence of artistic research as an institutional discourse. It remains to be seen whether and how the current efforts – above all from sites of higher education and scientific funding institutions – to push the connection between art and science can actually serve to promote the development of critical epistemologies and alternative or wild forms of knowledge production that intentionally or unintentionally oppose a technocratic-instrumental and accumulation-oriented notion of knowledge.

In this context, as someone employed within academic art education with an administrative role, and also being involved in inventing institutional structures in the field of artistic research, I am especially curious about forms or dimensions of knowledge that don't easily lend themselves to processes of capitalisation. One of many inspiring conceptions in this regard is a psychoanalytically informed comprehension of knowledge and of insight as an intersubjective event, "an act, a process of narration".[14] Years ago, Shoshana Felman described knowledge that cannot be exchanged as an "analytic (textual) knowledge" because it has to be used and is different in every case, depending on the singularity of the corresponding event:

> Analytic (textual) knowledge cannot be exchanged, it has to be used – and used in each case differently, according to the singularity of the case, according to the specificity of the text. Textual or analytic knowledge is, in other words, that peculiar knowledge which, unlike any commodity, is subsumed by its *use* value, having no exchange value whatsoever.[15]

Felman's argument is based on an engagement with the materiality of language in its symbolic structure and describes a knowledge that emerges both within the process and for the process of interpretation. Therefore, it is knowledge that emerges in the making – in an engagement with specific materials and materialities. I would like to extend this understanding of knowledges generated both in and for the making from an analytic/textual knowledge towards an analytic/material-semiotic knowledge. This shift is also motivated by a thought that arose during an interview with the artist Stefanie Seibold. It was formulated as we discussed the idea often circulating within contemporary texts on art and theories of capitalism, that today's post-conceptual art production is no longer based on manual skills but on immaterial (intellectual) skills, which finally allow the manual part of a working process to be outsourced elsewhere. Could be, says Stefanie Seibold, however:

> You need a certain amount of experience in creating and making things yourself in order to later say how you actually want to have something – that is the form of thinking that is necessary for these works. Through a process of making and then throwing away, and then making something else, and through seeing the colours you gain significant insight. Making is also a way of thinking with materials, forms, and content. Making is thinking.[16]

I emphasise this analytic/material-semiotic notion of knowledge in order to counter a tendency that treats the material practices of text-producing scientists in the field of artistic research as a template for everybody else. More conceptual flexibility is certainly called for here, also from funding authorities, so that designs for funding programmes, as well as their application materials and yearly report forms, don't only follow the classical standard of (natural) scientific production as they, for instance, make sure to request the registration of patents but might forget to enable the uploading of pictures. Also administrators and managers of institutions that house artistic research projects will have to participate in imagining artistic research beyond the science paradigm. Otherwise, situations won't stop occurring where those working on an artistic research project are asked what else they could possibly need but a desk and a computer: "...since, you are only doing research?"[17]

After having worked through these errors in translation, surely a more courageous framework of representation can be found in order to enable an understanding of artistic research that is also a practice in and of diverse materialities, that tries out forms of collaboration, that experiments with formats of publication and therefore also with forms of the public.

As an intellectual activity, this research practice is based on an engagement with questions of form as questions of materialisation, and therefore it encourages shifting the prevailing notion of knowledge towards conceptions of materialism/experimentalism, to thinking as making/acting/practice.[18] And since materialisation is about generating reality, it is therefore also always about transforming reality.

1
Interview with Tom Holert, Vienna, 25 November 2010. For the research project visit: www.troublingresearch.net.

2
A short derivation of these processes, especially in relation to the Academy of Fine Arts Vienna's PhD in Practice programme can be found here: http://blogs.akbild.ac.at/phdinpractice/phd-in-practice/faqs/.

3
For a short presentation of the PhD in Practice participants and their projects, see http://blogs.akbild.ac.at/phdinpractice/phd-in-practice/participants/.

4
For Michael Baers' text resulting from this research see http://www.e-flux.com/journal/view/233.

5
Interview with Michael Baers, Vienna, 25 March 2011.

6
www.troublingresearch.net.

7
Kathrin Busch, 'Knowledge in the Arts – A Philosophical Daydream', tr. Gerrit Jackson, in *Texte zur Kunst*, 20/82 (2011), 73.

8
Cf. Alex Demirović, 'Die Zerstörung wissenschaftlicher Rationalität in der gegenwärtigen Hochschulreform', in *Bund demokratischer Wissenschaftlerinnen und Wissenschaftler (BdWi) / freier zusammenschluss von studentInnenschaften (fzs): Studiengebühren, Elitekonzeptionen & Agenda 2010* (Marburg: 2004), <http://www.studis-online.de/HoPo/Bildungsstreik/hochschulreform.php?seite=2>, accessed 18 July 2011.

9
Cf., e.g., Hito Steyerl, 'Aesthetics of Resistance? Artistic Research as Discipline and Conflict', *eipcp* (January 2010), <http://eipcp.net/transversal/0311/steyerl/en>, accessed 18 July 2011.

10
Conversation with Michael Baers, Vienna, 25 March 2011.

11
Ibid.

12
Interview with Mika Hannula, Berlin, 22 September 2010.

13
Alex Demirović, 'Die Zerstörung wissenschaftlicher Rationalität'.

14
Shoshana Felman, *Jacques Lacan and the Adventures of Insight. Psychoanalysis in Contemporary Culture* (Cambridge: Harvard University Press, 1987), 4.

15
Ibid., 81.

16
Interview with Stefanie Seibold, Vienna, 16 March 2011.

17
Troubling Research answered this question in an open letter to the Academy's rectorate/management entitled 'Some Exercise in Complex Seeing Is Needed': *A Space for Communication*. We need a space that invites people to be communicative and to communicate. Communication happens with and along experimental materialities and visualities. Thus, we also need *a space for experimentation* for artistic production, i.e., the possibility of a material-artistic-visual production has to be provided for. We need a spatial situation that allows for experimenting with installing sounds, images, and visual archives. In general, a spatial situation is required that invites visual and material experimentation. Finally, *a space for the public*: We need to be able to generate some kind of public. We need to be able to have regular events (workshops, performances, playing records, presentations, discussion rounds) for around 50-80 people.

18
Cf. Richard Sennett, *The Craftsman* (New Haven: Yale University Press, 2008) and Donna Haraway, 'The Promises of Monsters: A Regenerative Politics for Inappropriate/d Others', in Lawrence Grossberg, Cary Nelson, and Paula A. Treichler (eds.), *Cultural Studies* (New York: Routledge, 1992), 295–337.

Works by → Michael Bachhofer, Alin Cîrstea, Pepa Bugueiro Domingo, Sarah Duit, Romana Egartner, Anna Fatér, Rudolf Friemel, Michaela Grass, Martin Leopold Groedl, Ashley Holwell, Anna Fríða Jónsdóttir, Michal Marencik, Iulian Moise, David Palme, Leon Ploszczanski, Richard Schwarz, Manuel Stark, Sabina Teichert, Beniamin Urbanek, Brigitte Zwick

parameter{world}
parameters for every or no thing
→ An exhibition of Art & Science
30.3.–1.4.2011.

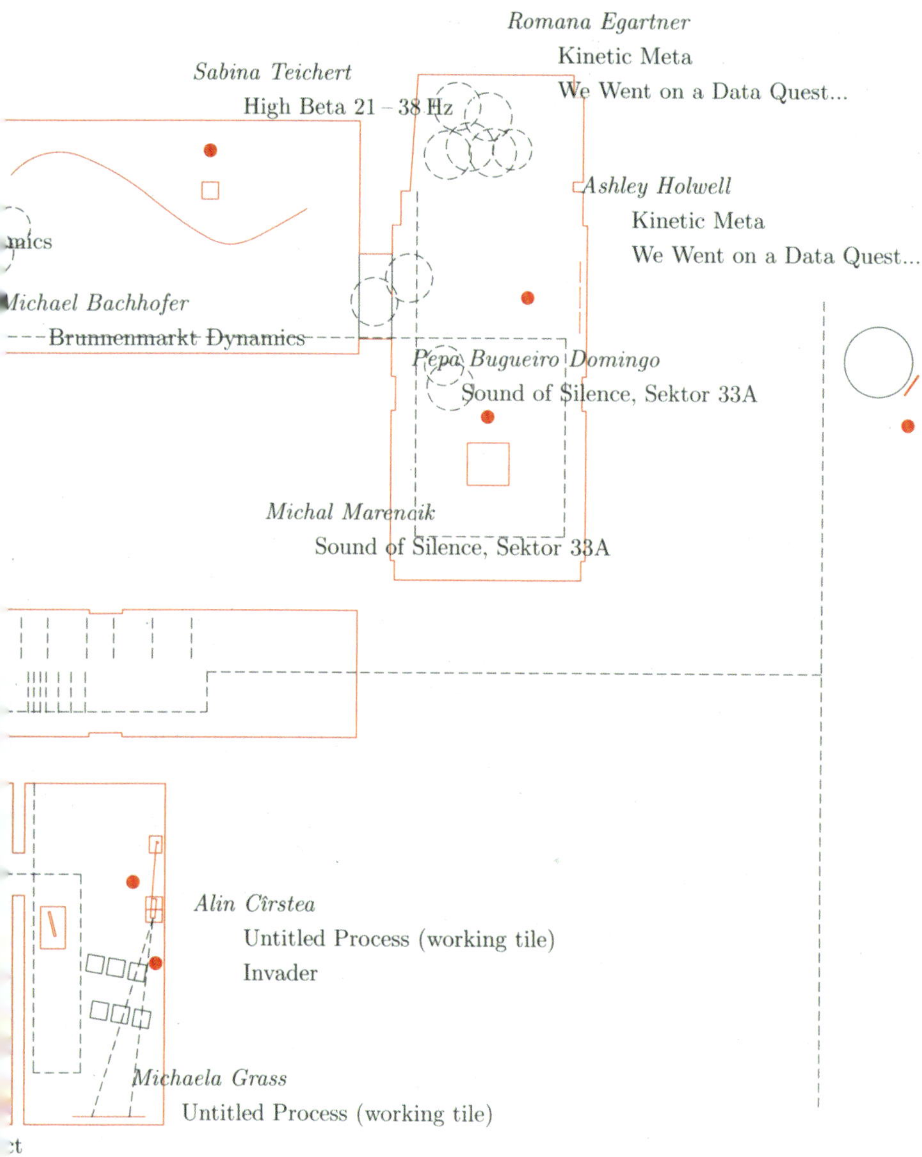
Romana Egartner
Kinetic Meta
We Went on a Data Quest...
Sabina Teichert
High Beta 21 – 38 Hz
Ashley Holwell
Kinetic Meta
We Went on a Data Quest...
mics
Michael Bachhofer
Brunnenmarkt Dynamics
Pepa Bugueiro Domingo
Sound of Silence, Sektor 33A
Michal Marenčík
Sound of Silence, Sektor 33A
Alin Cîrstea
Untitled Process (working tile)
Invader
Michaela Grass
Untitled Process (working tile)
t

4.5

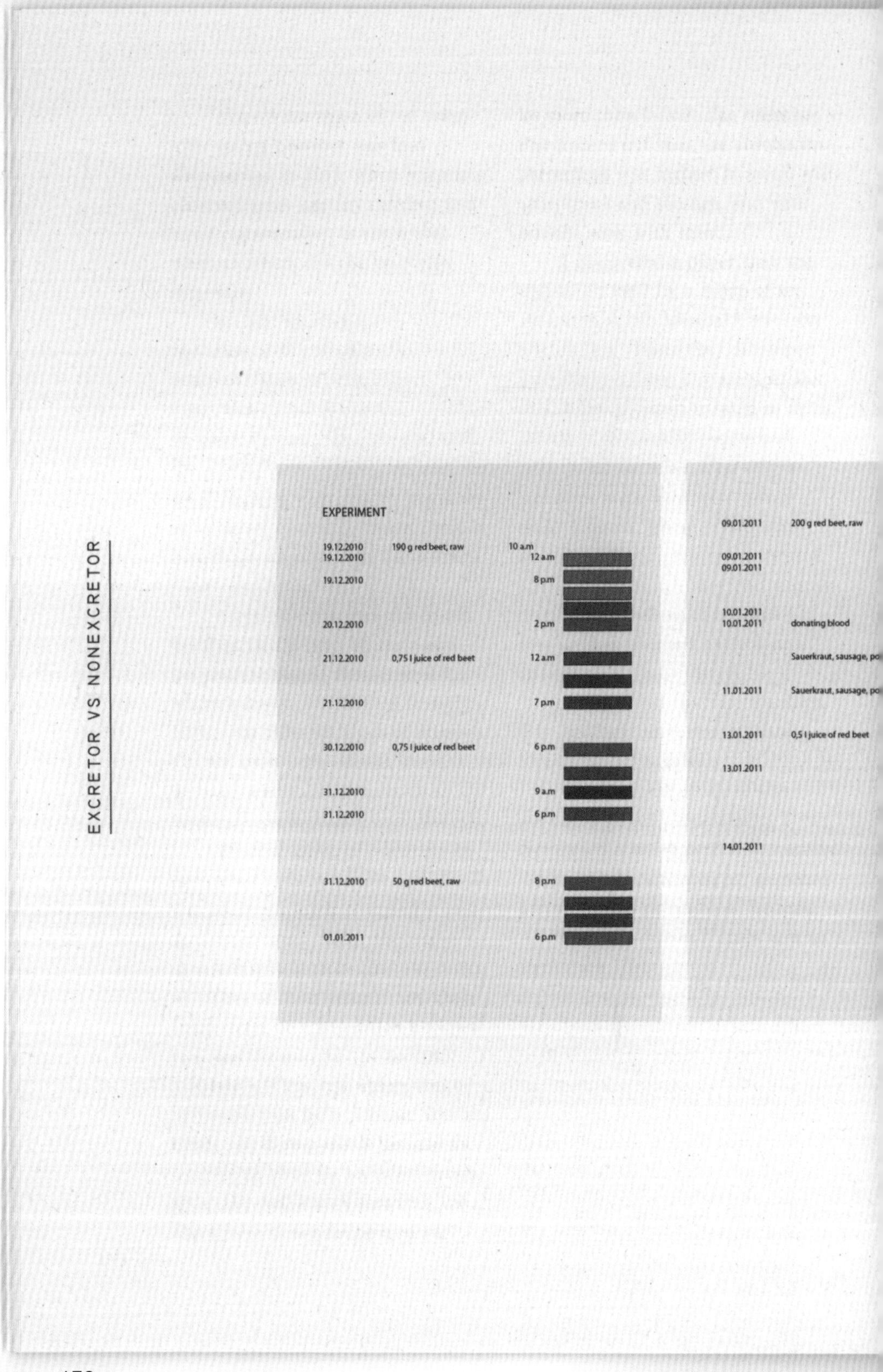

EXCRETOR VS NONEXCRETOR

EXPERIMENT

19.12.2010	190 g red beet, raw	10 a.m
19.12.2010		12 a.m
19.12.2010		8 p.m
20.12.2010		2 p.m
21.12.2010	0,75 l juice of red beet	12 a.m
21.12.2010		7 p.m
30.12.2010	0,75 l juice of red beet	6 p.m
31.12.2010		9 a.m
31.12.2010		6 p.m
31.12.2010	50 g red beet, raw	8 p.m
01.01.2011		6 p.m

09.01.2011	200 g red beet, raw
09.01.2011	
09.01.2011	
10.01.2011	
10.01.2011	donating blood
	Sauerkraut, sausage, po
11.01.2011	Sauerkraut, sausage, po
13.01.2011	0,5 l juice of red beet
13.01.2011	
14.01.2011	

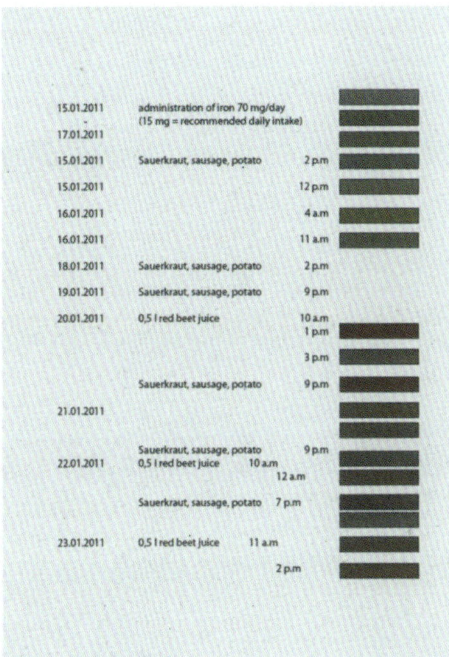

12,13

Brigitte Zwick
C-Print, Wooden Box with Urine Samples

The installation shows an adapted representation of the subway and passenger paths of the Viennese subway system. It should empower the visitor to "play" with the underlying data, which had been collected and used to create this work.

Artistic Research gets more and more important in every field of specialization. Not just in terms of "humanizing" otherwise cold technology but also to open our minds for new ideas and approaches, which can lead to far more than just simplicity. This installation wants to show the principles of Artistic Research: To observe and work with data in an unbiased, artistic way. The setting allows the clean "saving" of a constellation created by the user, via photography or documentation, kind of like scientists isolate key features to carry out their theories afterwards. The visible horizontal ring should preserve the original orientation of the ground level. This particular framework for the data representation should also be seen as a statement to Bruno Latour's idea of a black box – the underlying data gets visible by opening the blackbox around it. But imagine riding the subway – virtually being inside the black box, taking the system for granted – you will see that black boxes often can and should be opened from within.

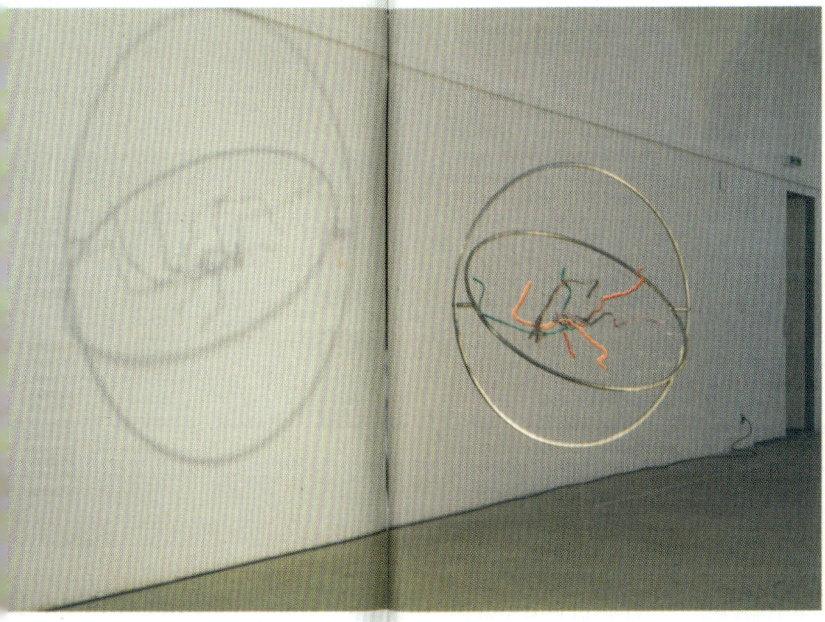

14.15

THE SOUND OF SILENCE. SEKTOR 33. COMPOSITION UPON THE ZENTRALFRIEDHOF

"Say a number between one and ten," one of us asked the waitress That is how our work at Wien Bestattung (municipal funeral director) started. She reacted with, "Was? What?" and then said, "Six", six euros for two melanges.

That same day, echoed answers following interviews, bewilderment, the looming fear of the metaphysical, fragile compass of the endeavour. "Six" was just number on a list...
→ *we awoke in the Zentralfriedhof...*
Finitude. An existence obsessed with an end. Bare life, aesthetics of death, of life. A feeling belonging to the Romanticism? Unbreakable silences, severe textures... the design of mass cemeteries outside the city! Perhaps a great example of the architecture of death, Vienna's is the most populated in Europe. In its time commissioned to draw a frontier between the living and the *malade* dead, trees growing a border designed, masked, as an ambitious garden...
→ *we awoke in the Zentralfriedhof...*
C prelude / a frontier fence / tor 1, 2, sektor, sektor, 33A / a sequence of gravestones / *1:4 on death* / wonder of Western exposure / *2:4 fieldwork at the graveyard* / inert, reserved rest / digits of gone lives / the underground, the wells of / *3:4 silence* / inert map / voids noted on paper / melodised / not altered! / *4:4 the interpreter* / depicts a partiture / resonates / on / finitude, eternal repetition

The techniques of reducing faces to lines and blending a group of single "stroke-faces" into one have beenemployed in a search for facial expressions that have become inscribed in our faces (the social face). There is also a cultural-anthropological interest involved here as it is a method to trace the inconspicuous in a culture. Often extreme examples indicate something random, which upon closer inspection turn out to be everyday phenomena. This explains the look at North Korea, or at the controlled face of a politician, or at the front view of cars: What does it mean when the image of a politician features many dark areas, suggesting a modest repertoire of facial expressions? Or what if the resulting front views appear quite aggressive?

Perhaps stereotypical facial expressions – bound to certain socially established images – have been disseminated by the media and become imprinted in our minds, causing us to "look" so alike?

Reading the face of society, which might be looking at us – and we smile back?

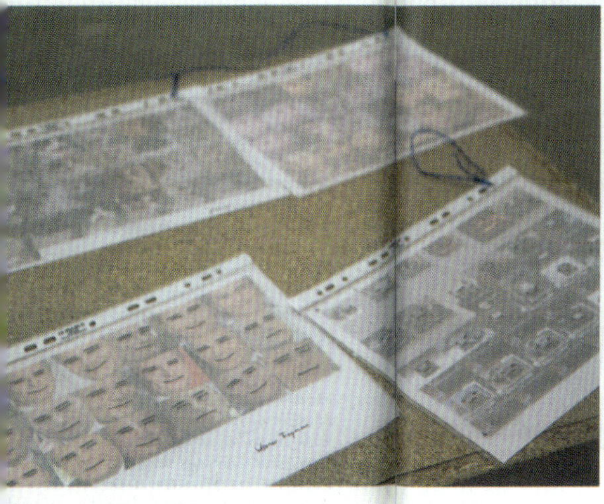

28,29

Richard Schwarz
Digital Print

HIGH BETA 21-38 HZ

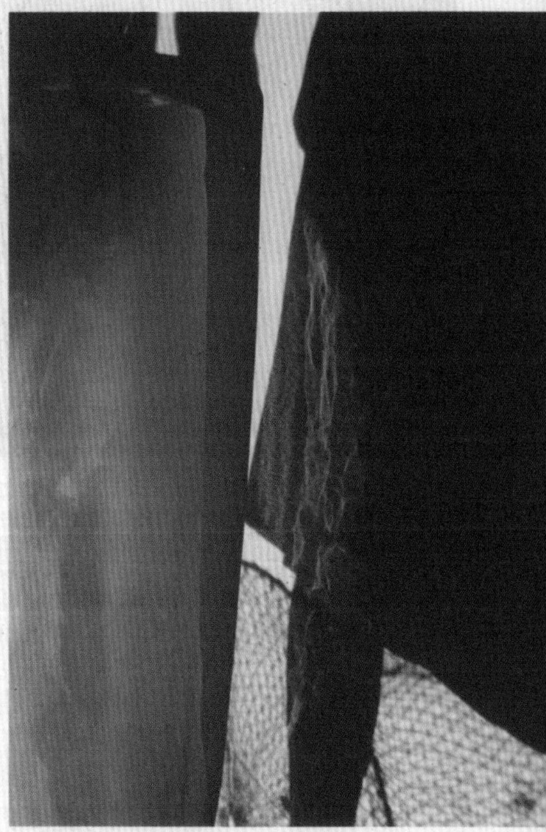

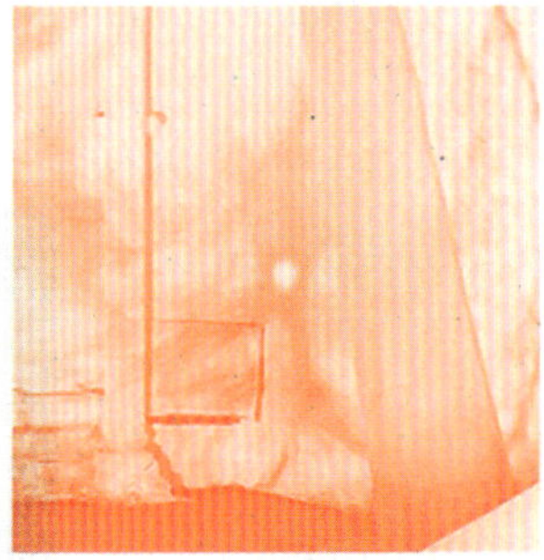

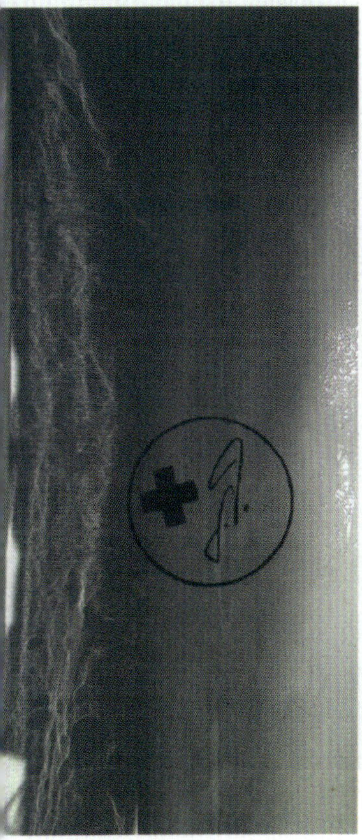

34.35

Sabina Teichert
'Metaxü', reuse, ice cubes, slide projection

THOUGHT INTERPRETER

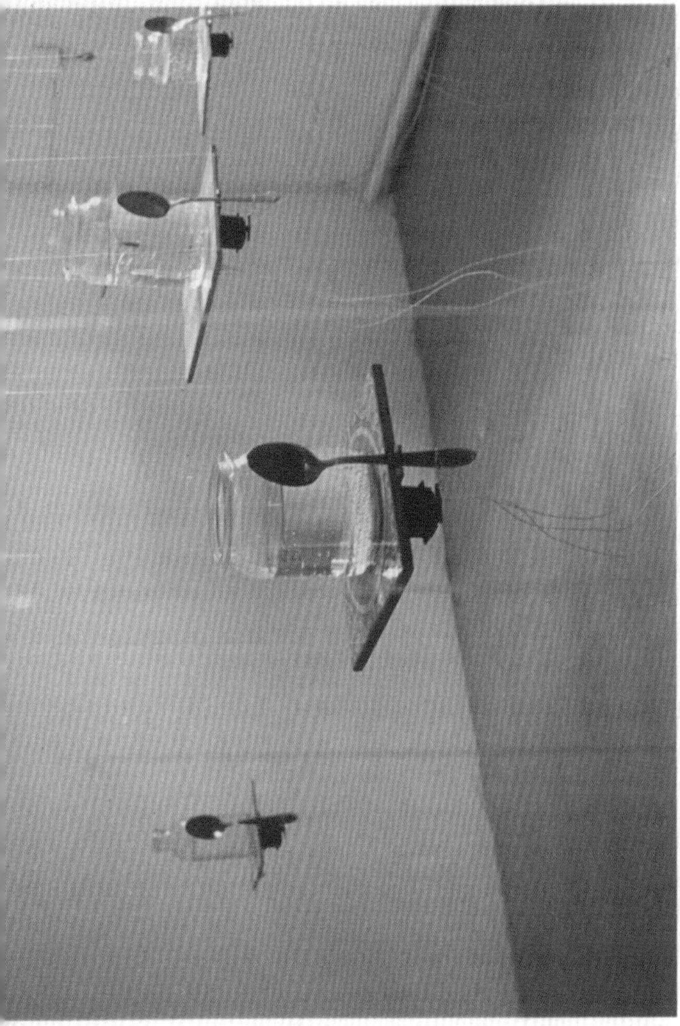

36,37

INVADER

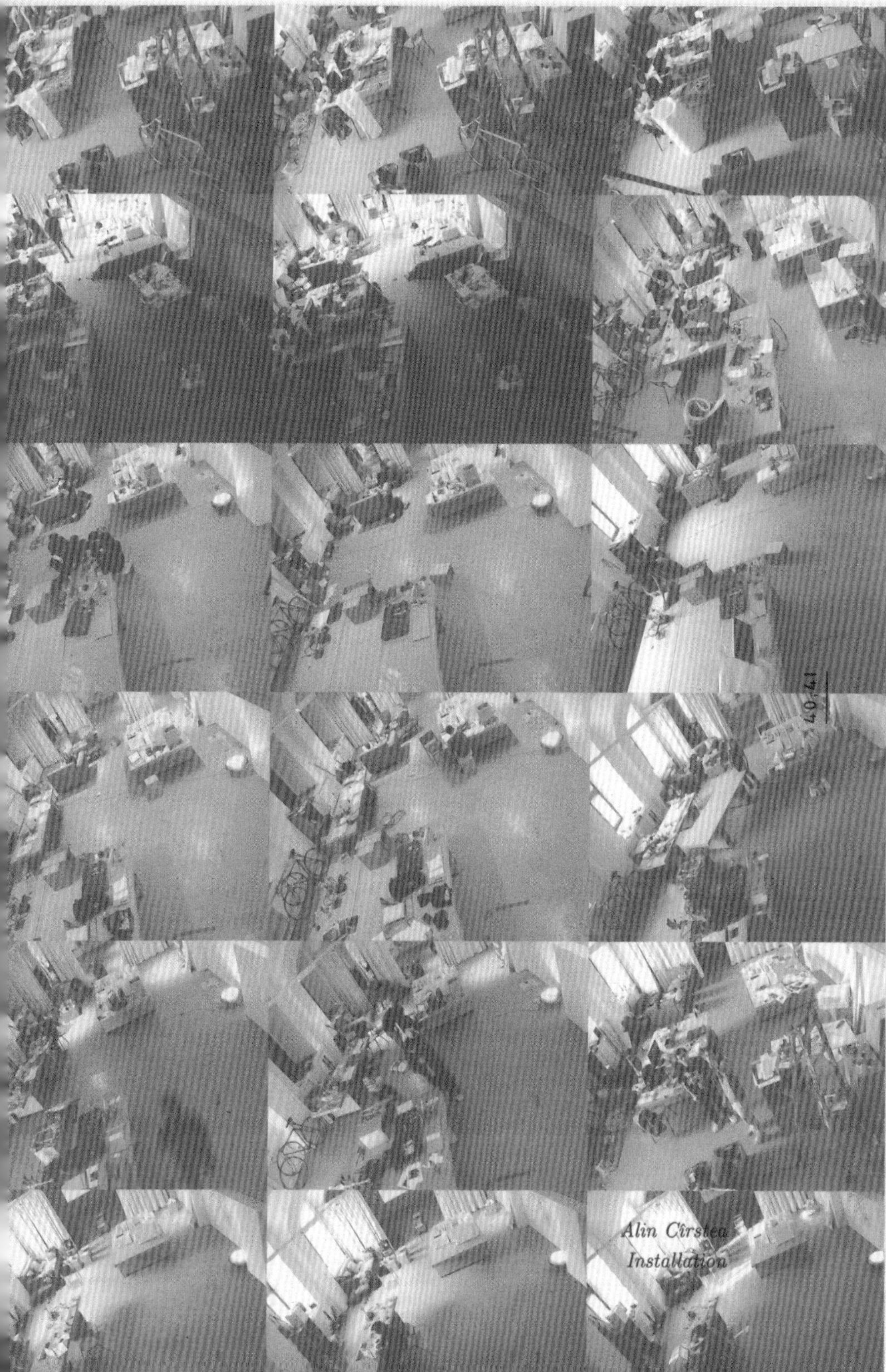

Alin Cîrstea
Installation

42,43

I create them without thinking. It's me alone who knows when they are finished and then I just look at them and smile. What else do I need?

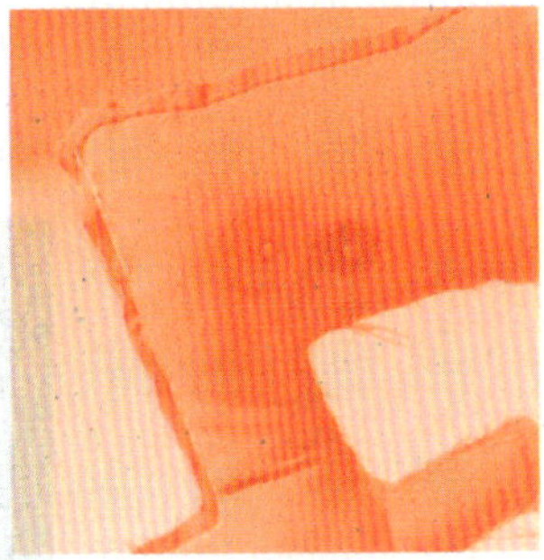

52,53

Beniamin Urbanek
Monsterragdolls exposed somewhere in a room

Egograms is a series of graphs – visual records – of numerous actions the artist undertook, dealing with reflection and self-awareness.

The resulting works act as personal diagrams. They can be considered self-portraits in the broadest sense, but they also touch on the nature of scientific data generation, fact making, memory, and the problem of objectivity.

Exhibited works included →

'Autographs Series', 'What goes down...', 'Autoportrait 1', 'Egogram', 'Atopic Consciousness (23.3.2011 13:34:08, Bodhgaya)' and 'Fig. 1'.

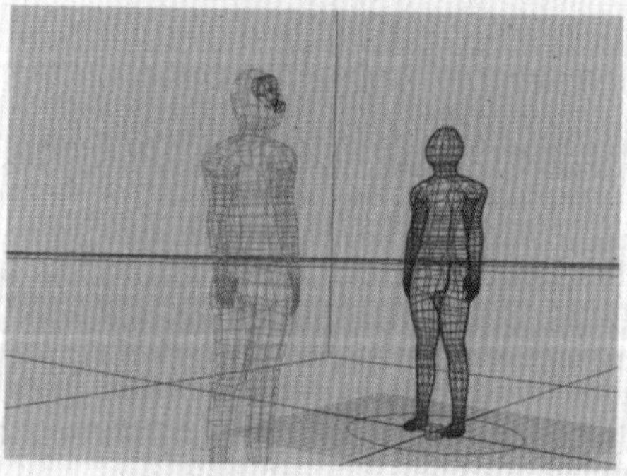

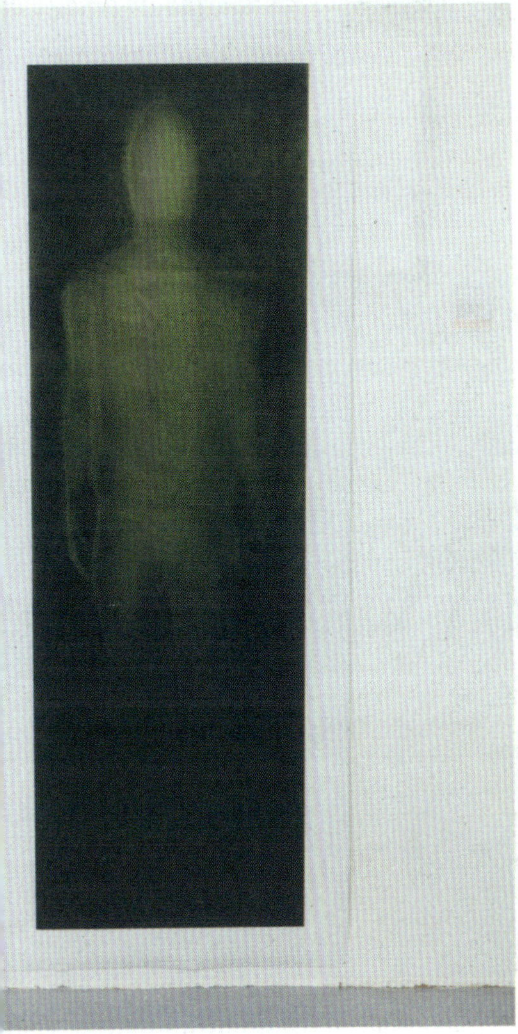

48,49

Martin Leopold Groedl
Digital Prints

KINETIC META

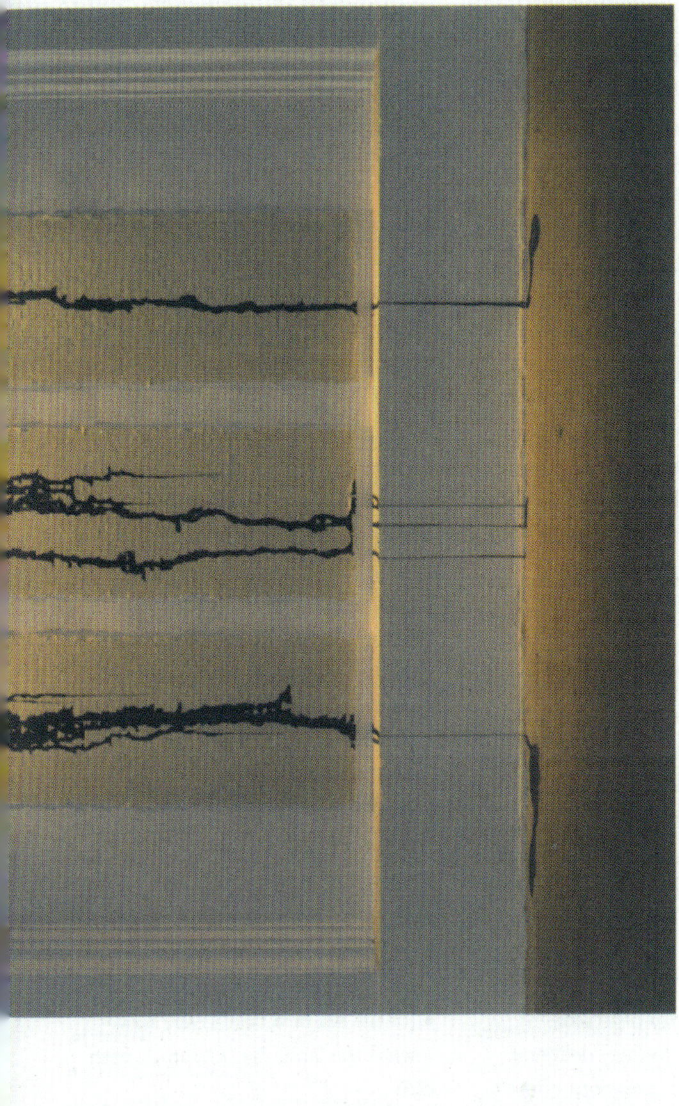

54,55

Q: We could be going down completely different paths?

A: Statistics NZ operates on a cost recovery basis which means there is a charge for customised information.

A: Statistics Netherlands has figures concerning the population.

However not as specific as you are requering[sic] for.

A: Thank you for your request. Unfortunately, I do not see a possibility to provide you with any data of the type you are looking for.

A: The answer was that they do not keep data on the place of birth, and that they would not transmit any address data, for these are protected data.

A: One aspect I forgot to mention yesterday: ReportPortal (downloads ? and) uses a library msxmlapi.dll. For some of our customers this has caused a problem. Usually it´s concerned with security settings, and it is solved by marking RotterdamDATA as a trusted site. In rare cases it is the firewall that prevents downloading or using msxmlapi.dll.

A: By principle, I do not see any problems concerning your request.

A: Here you go!

Q: Out of questioning there should be an interaction?

60,61

Romana Egartner, Ashley Holwell
Archive entry

An array of 10 audio speakers represents the variety of sounds at Vienna's Brunnenmarkt from 4 am when the setup of the stands begins until 7 pm when trading stops.

In this globalised world the seasonal rhythm of product availability has almost disappeared. 24-hour supermarkets all around the world don't show any kind of rhythm. Supply of products is hidden; actors are anonymous. Traditional markets like the Brunnenmarkt provide us with a rich variety of life and personality. Within this increasingly artificial world, market life provides a biologically important rhythm.

The density of noise at the market varies dramatically during the day, although the maximum amplitude does not change much. The sound of plastic bags is conspicuous in the busy phases. Conversation, including non-market related subjects, is an important part of such places.

The installation's arrangement allows for different perceptions of the recordings. The volume is intentionally set low to invite listeners to come close and listen carefully. Single samples tell stories about the actors involved, while the complete set of recordings gives an impression of the market's overall dynamic.

We believe that our method helps to give better insight into the dynamic of a multivariate place like the Brunnenmarkt.

62,63

MUSICTERIA

Music has a strong influence on living beings, including plants, animals, and, of course, humans. The ways in which they are affected might differ (be it physical, biological, psychological, social), but they all still seem to respond to the stimulus. Why should one of the smallest organisms on Earth, bacteria, be exempt from this principle? In an approach to pinpoint their reaction, we tested lactic acid bacteria with different kinds of music while they did their work producing yoghurt from milk. Our hypothesis was that this would influence the growth rate or metabolism of the bacteria, which would also have an effect on the taste of milk products.

For our yoghurt production facility we built a sound and temperature isolation box equipped with loudspeakers; yoghurt bacteria were cultivated in pre-warmed milk in this environment. Each culture was exposed to one of three different kinds of music or kept in a silent environment for 8 hours, a period in which the process of milk turning into yoghurt should be completed. We checked the pH of the milk samples every two hours and stored the final yoghurt in the fridge. Repeated pH measurements did not support the hypothesis of a major musical influence on bacterial growth. Still, tasters accounted for significant differences in taste in the final products. This elicits several questions of taste generation and perception.

96,4 % COPPER

A fascination with the different surfaces that are produced in a galvanic process, which has been used since a long time to plate jewellery with silver and gold, and the works of Tassilo Blittersdorff inspired my experimental setup with galvanisation.

My aim was to move away from the usual pictures the setup would produce and dive into the variety of ultrastructures built in the 'hell kitchen' of a galvanic bath – a re-enactment of a medieval alchemist's laboratory, but utilising electron microscopy.

The first results gained from the analysis with the Scanning Electron Microscope (SEM) displayed structures similar to flowers, some more like corals, and others had the shape of little molecule stick models along with typical copper crystals.

The main focus of my ongoing research will be to discover if the growth of crystals can be reproduced and predicted. The difficulty therein is that the crystallisation process in galvanisation is influenced by a number of parameters, which are highly indistinguishable and indeterminable. My starting point is to vary the direct current and confirm by means of SEM images whether there is a change in the ultrastructure. By using different voltage supply sources, a limited influence in the growth process of the crystallization might be visible under the electron microscope.

74,75

Leon Ploszczanski
Research on Galvanic Process

I'm covered with the blood of Jesus is a fragment of *bloodworks*, a series of projects that deals with the work of Alexander Bogdanov, a Russian pioneer in the realms of blood transfusion and system theory. In the autumn of 2009, a "blood miracle" transpired in Bogdanov's birthplace Sokolka. During the Holy Mass, a sacramental host fell from the hand of the priest. According to Catholic customs, such consecrated hosts cannot be simply thrown away. It must be kept in holy water in a special liturgical vessel, a ciborium, until it dissolves. After 14 days, the priest opened the ciborium and discovered therein a red fluid with little blood-red chunks. For him, it was clear: It was a blood miracle. The miracle was quickly sent for analysis to two different laboratories. Both established that the material in the fluid was human heart tissue – tissue from a heart that stopped beating under severe stress. Later on, it became apparent that the sample was not human heart tissue rather it originated from a bacteria strain that would take on a major role in the history of the blood wonder: the bacteria "serratia marcescens".

For the work *I'm covered with the blood of Jesus*, this bacteria was cultured specifically on sacramental hosts in order to test the reproducibility of a blood miracle under laboratory conditions. And with success. However, it must be mentioned that it is not a trivial task to create the impression of blood. It required roughly a half year's work and over 160 attempts with different cultures from the strain in order to obtain the desired result. In retrospect, one can safely say that it is, in fact, a small miracle when this rare bacterium develops exactly to this point in non-laboratory conditions. Mind you, not a "blood miracle". *(Exhibited at The Essence, 2011; MAK Vienna)*

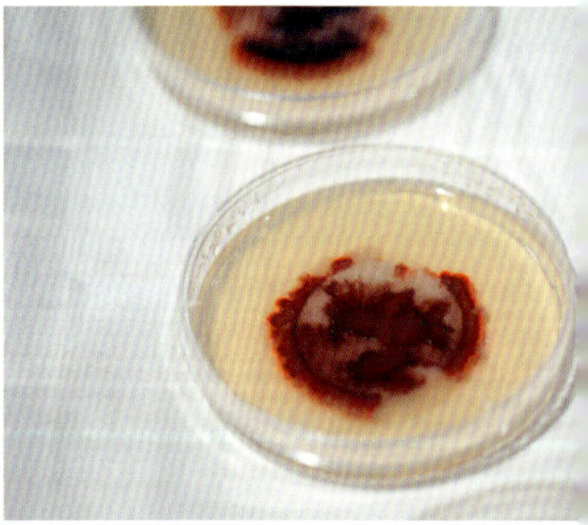

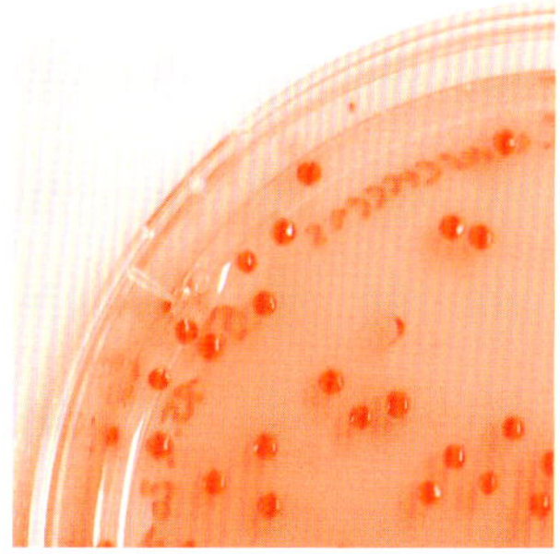

Wolfang Schwarzenbrunner
Bacterial Sculpture

Hans Christian Andersen's fairy tale *The Emperor's New Clothes* is the departure point for this installation of glass, which links the visible and the invisible to one another. To the naked eye the installation is transparent; only with further indirection do the true colours become apparent. *(Master project, 2011. Exhibited at The Essence, 2011; MAK Vienna)*

0,0

Andrea Weidlich
Glass Installation

EPILOGUE

PARAMETER{WORLD}

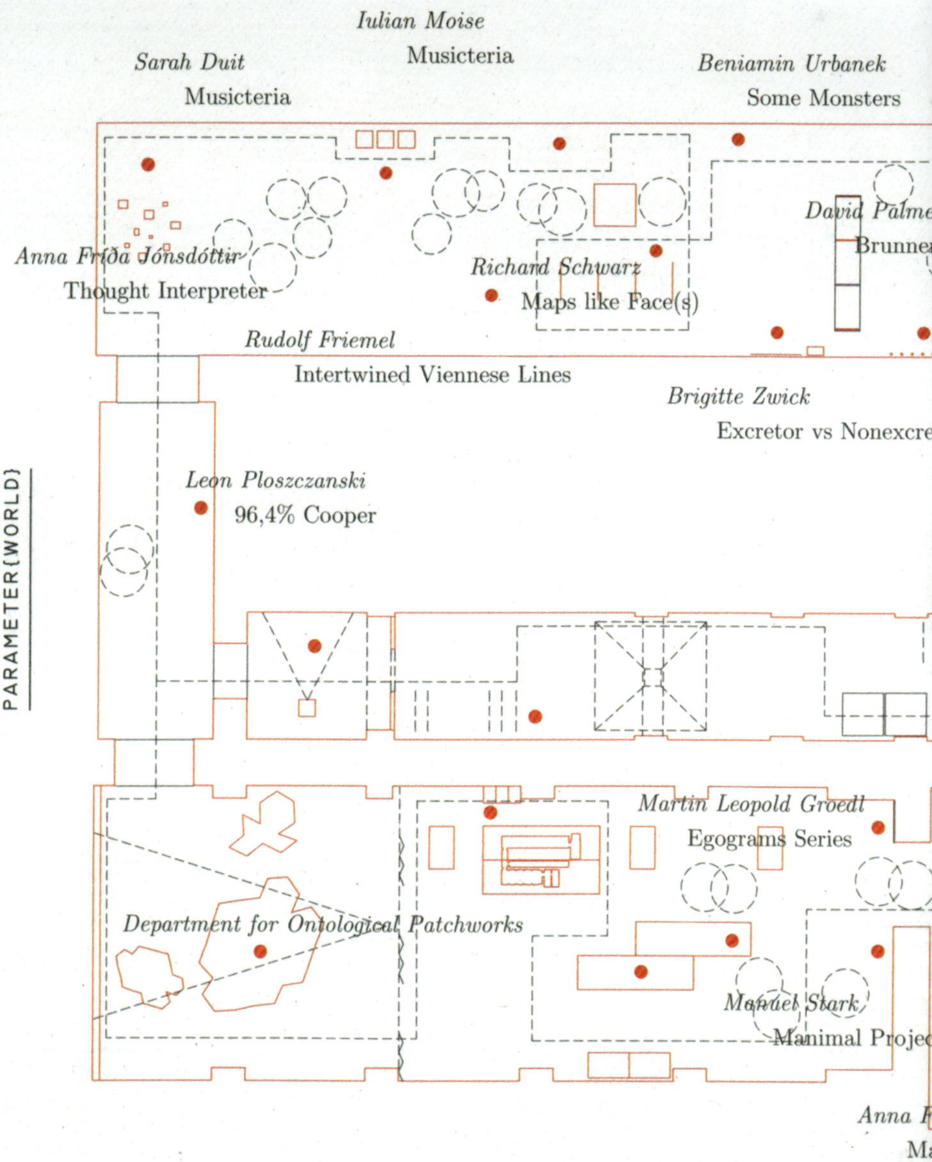

Virgil Widrich – What do you do?

In life it is not possible to have an answer for every question, but it is better to have an answer for questions one expects to be asked. Human beings, always driven by curiosity, sometimes ask: "What do you do?" either when they want to be polite or when they really want to know. And when I am polite, too, and present them an honest answer about what I do at the Angewandte, the next question – usually louder – goes like "what is this Art & Science thing?" And this is precisely where we enter the terrifying territory of the expected questions I should have an answer for. One way to avoid embarrassment is to not bring up the subject in the first place, but this is hardly an option given the publication you have in your hands at the moment. One could also concentrate on the differences between art and science, which are clearer than their similarities: bad science can kill you, bad art cannot. Being at an art university, an island in an otherwise spoiled and bankrupt world, one could also recall the film *The Draughtsman's Contract*,[1] which proves so nicely that people can lie, but art always has to tell the truth. With Michael Nyman's beautiful music in the inner ear, one has to come to the conclusion that asking people is not a good idea if you want to get honest results. Maybe we should rather ask the works being created in our class: The answer might be found there. So, what happened in our final semester presentation on 28 June 2011 from 9:37 to 15:54?

Michaela Grass and Alin Cîrstea studied the history of optical synthetic sound, which was hand drawn on film in the 1920s, 30s, and 40s by artists like Oskar Fischinger or Norman McLaren. They mixed this concept with contemporary computer eye-tracking and a software that can tranform those tracks into audio. The result is a sound created not by the drawing hand but by the looking eye. Michaela and Alin's work shows once again that film mixes well with other spheres, maybe because it is the most interdisciplinary art form itself and – like an octopus – always finds something to hold.

Which brings us to plants and to the young field of bioart, an important scope for art and science: Rudolf Friemel proposed a bio-fictional art installation for the Vienna Artweek due in November 2011[2]: He attempts to create – from technology – believable biology manifested in the form of a plant, which would follow the watcher's movements in the Museum of Natural History in Vienna with big, curious eyes.

Iulian Moise, coming from a background in filmmaking and editing, presented the concept for a "floating spherical projection apparatus": a flying cinema on a balloon projecting what it films live on the ground. Iulian studied the history and the function of balloons, projection techniques, and the mathematical problems that occur when throwing flat images on curved surfaces. His project, like some others, extends the senses and reminds me of the "flying moon machines" in *A.I.*[3], which function like flying watchtowers over citizens of the future.

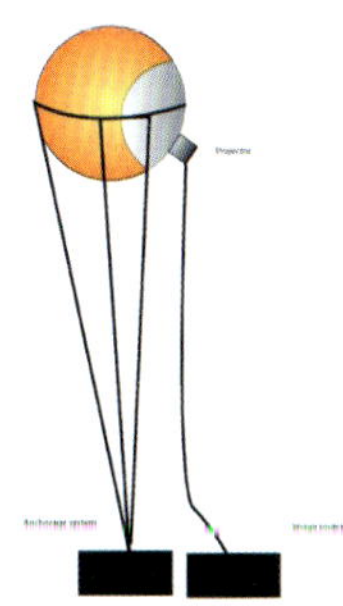

In his project "unconscious subversion", David Palme collected photos of makeshift fixes for everyday life problems. Without showing them directly, his work makes visible the people who live behind the flawless surfaces of modern life and try to solve problems that did not occur to the architects when they presented their perfect 3D renderings of future cities to their investors.

Manuel Stark, also looking for art and science in the sphere of bioart, created a concept for "deconstructing bioart", which involves pictures being made and dissolved by coloured bacteria that form the image's pixels.

Michal Marencik presented several different takes for interventions at the Museum of Natural History in Vienna: "Bacteriophage" is an installation comprised of large bacteriophages connected to small medicine pipes on the wall in which liquids circulate. "Planetorium/Florum" is a concept for an outdoor installation located on a rooftop, while "bird's perspective" and "context mapper" are two proposals involving balloons and laser beams.

Could theatre have anything to do with art and science? Sarah Duit and Anna Fatér undertook the monumental task of creating a theatre, writing a play for it, and performing the lives of "non-ordinary people in an ordinary world" with puppets. The idea came to them after a visit to the Federal Pathologic Anatomical Museum in the Viennese Narrenturm[4] and resulted in scenes of a six-legged woman on her bike, a two-headed girl trying to put her children to sleep, and a foetus thinking about how his future parents will look like.

Anna Fríða Jónsdóttir made our studio into a stage and gave a lively lecture performance on her thoughts about an "open/closed human system" involving Kirilian photography[5], cancer detection, and the – whenever impossible supernatural phenomena are to be discovered – unavoidable master performer Nicola Tesla[6].

"Changing visibility" was the title of Romana Egartner's presentation: She studied lichens under UV-light on white and black backgrounds and created natural effects resembling a nightly wood, a technique James Cameron would be happy to use for *Avatar II*. Her creation of an aura for plants was like an extension of Anna Fríða Jónsdóttir's performance on Kirilian photography.

In her second project on that intense day, Anna Fatér showed us "Acoustic Vienna" and her "sound diary in pictures", which is a collection of photos and well-drawn cartoons on acoustic incidents in Vienna's second district. Again, picture and sound are mixed in an inventive way, just like in the project by Michaela Grass and Alin Cîrstea, although Anna's pictures leave their movement to the viewer's imagination.

The field of "cognitive mapping" has engaged Michael Bachhofer for many years, resulting in a discussion on how this scientific mental processing model could be applied to artistic projects. In the timeframe we had during the presentations, a precise solution escaped us, but the discussion started a new process for Michael to be developed further in the coming months.

No monitor yet is big enough for Ashley Holwell's presentation: He concluded the day with a large print out of his project "...we went on a data quest", a collection of research on thoughts, containers, and their arbitrary and/or defined connections. This could be a form of cognitive mapping searched for a minute ago under the influence of Michael Bachhofer's thoughts.

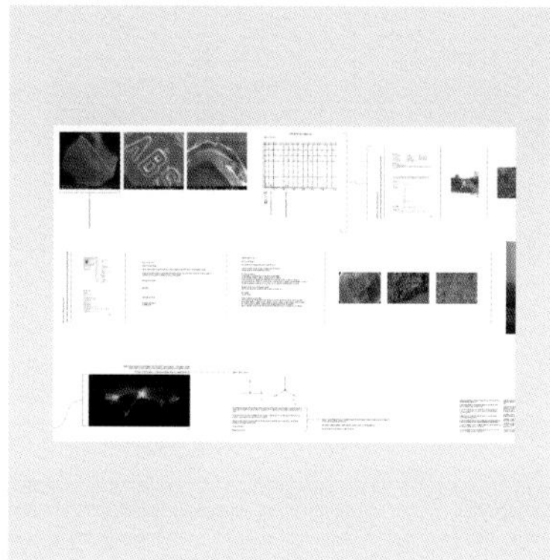

1
The Draughtsman's Contract, dir. Peter Greenaway (British Film Institute, 1982).

2
During the Vienna Artweek, students of the Art & Science master programme are invited to take part in this project, a cooperation of the University of Applied Arts and the Museum of Natural History. www.viennaartweek.at/2011/.

3
A.I. Artificial Intelligence, dir. Steven Spielberg (Warner Bros. Pictures, 2001).

4
Pathologisch-anatomisches Bundesmuseum. www.narrenturm.at.

5
Invented by Semyon Kirilian in 1939.

6
Nikola Tesla (1856–1943) was an inventor and engineer.

On this day, an exhausted audience of participants could see that works in the field of art and science can involve computers, films, theatre, plants, psychology, and even supernatural phenomena. As different as they may be, these works are the beginning of an answer to the question what art and science can be. Their creators took the risk of exchanging their known territory of artistic or scientific representational cultures with a space between the two where new and innovative splitters can be found. We tried to collect as many of them as we could find in our first four semesters of an institutionalised Art & Science programme.

Next time someone asks me "What do you do?" instead of talking about the Angewandte I could answer as a filmmaker and pitch my current animated feature film project: *Romeo and Julia in the microcosm of the human body: a forbidden love between the young bacteria Micromeo and the antibody girl Globia triggers a genetic catastrophe.*

It is relaxing that this project is completely different and has nothing to do with art and science. Absolutely nothing. Not a bit! So please don't ask me about this art and science thing!

Richard Schwarz On Drawing Lines

"Signifying by sounds and marks is an admirable abstraction. Three letters signify God for me – a few marks signify a million things."[1] With this remark, Novalis, a philosopher and German Romanticist writer, addressed the hopeful notion of reading the world through simple marks and lines. Moreover, it introduces a central hypothesis in this essayistic treatise of the line: The line functions as a sign that identifies and mediates *cut outs* of the world and refers to the details through a process of abstraction. In drawing a line one comes to the point, or at least to a relatively clear interpretation of the world. The space crossed by the line is divided into an over-here and an over-there, one space and the other. The line functions as a threshold for perception that assists in putting everything in place.[2] Through words and associations the intention in drawing a line becomes more apparent: It is an attempt to manifest the world in a line, to depict the meaning rather than the phenomenon in a condensed form.

This thought is well put by mathematician and poet George Spencer-Brown in his postulation to "draw a distinction". A distinction should be made as the beginning of all cognitive processes. Standardised operations can be seen anew by setting margins and differentiations.[3] This basic method is shared by sciences and arts, and with quite similar intentions. However, attempts to draw strict divisions are repeatedly found. For instance, the artistic view is said to be subjective whereas the sciences are deemed as being objective. By drawing a line between these ascriptions, one is forced to oscillate between these argued poles in relation to specific examples.

In the eighteenth century, the techniques of copper engravers shifted towards abstraction; describing the world through simple strokes became increasingly popular. But the early reproduction craftsmen didn't depict reality directly, rather they copied hundreds of model drawings to learn the method of abstraction before they were allowed to deal with nature directly.[4] These copyists had to learn how to use strokes in the right manner. The outcome was a "net of rationality"[5] guided by strict rules. With the technique of cross-hatching every surface could be represented, be it the waves of the sea or the feathers of the seabird. Every object was constructed by the same patterns and principles.[6]

Such constellations of lines tell about the becoming of an image and therefore about how reality is approached. According to the art historian Peter Assmann, a network of lines serves to include and exclude imaginary worlds, which is applicable in both writing and drawing. If a line appears by itself, the ambiguity is far greater; but an expressive line always preserves a trace of the context of its making.[7] Following these observations, artistic or scientific notions of a line can be reconciled. In an artistic context, one would read a line as an "emotional signal", whereas in a scientific context the line would be a representation of nature, a diagrammatic visualisation of data. In both cases, however, one can describe the line as a retrievable archive of memory. Perceptions and concepts become more utilisable through lines and strokes. Whether in a drawing or a diagram, they are not only a means to save a thought; they also create a new idea or way of perceiving through the depicted.

Drawn to Lines

The physicist Richard Feynman, an American pioneer in quantum field theory, also employed lines to note relations and resolve core issues in his research. Peter Galison describes Feynman's procedure: "Do you want to know how an electron goes from A to B? Then consider all the ways that you can draw diagrams of electrons, their emission and absorption

Fig. 1
Example of a "Feynman diagram" showing the case of an electron collision. On the basis of established physical laws, all cases (or as many as possible) are translated into lines to reduce them to mathematical equations.

of photons, and the intermediate production of electron-position pairs. Each piece of the diagram corresponded to a calculation rule, so when you finished drawing you had a straightforward mathematical problem to solve."[8] These calculated lines are delineations, indicators, and help to inspire solutions.

Nevertheless, there is a big difference between the motives of the copper engravers and those of the quantum theorist in their use of strokes and lines. And we have also bypassed an important change in the scientific exploration of the world: the path from the signature of a researcher – in notes and sketches – to the signature of nature, such as the nature prints of the nineteenth-century illustrator Alois Auer. In order to attain results without a human bias, images of plants, animals, rocks, and other natural subjects were produced through direct impressions on a copper plate press. A multitude of samples were used to create the depiction of, for example, *the* daisy as a typology, thereby creating artefacts with a hyperreal quality.

Another researcher who studied the signature of nature was the physiologist Étienne-Jules Marey. He described life as a mechanical process and the body as a machine. His research was devoted to discover the laws of locomotion in animals and humans. In movement Marey saw the crucial element of his research: "Motion is the most apparent of the characteristics of life; it manifests itself in all the functions, it is even the essence of several of them."[9] In order to preserve the dynamics of movement and to study them objectively, Marey used graphs to document the changes over a period of time. The "graphic method" he used is known from studies in other disciplines. For instance, the bishop and natural scientist Nicole d'Oresme already applied a similar method to analyse the laws of nature in the fourteenth century. However, in physiology it was a new approach that involved the development of complicated measurement devices in order to produce valid data and "to capture the movement without interfering with it or impoverishing

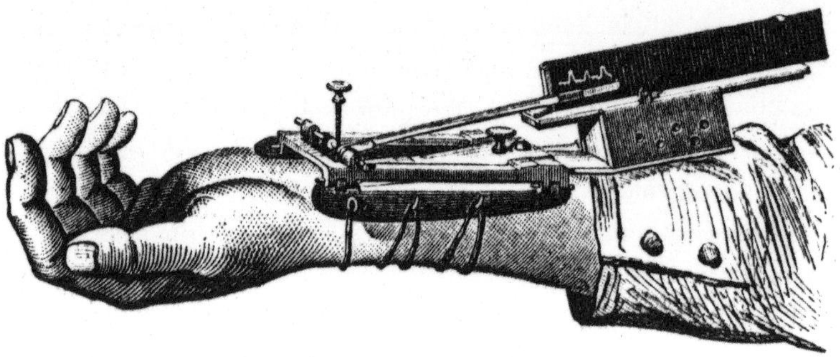

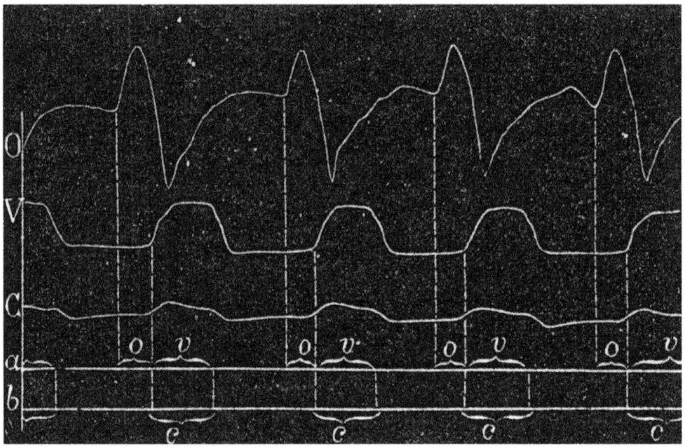

Fig. 2 & 3
Marey's sphygmograph visualises the pressure difference of the vascular wall in relation to the time passed. Thereby, the blood circulation is represented with a line. Above, the apparatus and at the bottom, one of the results.

it in any way".[10] The lines of the graphs drawn by the beating wing or pulse rate of a pigeon made it possible to apprehend a phenomenon that was otherwise unperceivable in real time. "This curve, which rises, falls, or remains stationary, shows what has really taken place much more clearly than a column of figures, which is tedious and fatiguing to read down."[11] The graph succeeds in summing up all observations and condensing them into a simple line. The line as the result of the measurements acts as a "satisfactory representation" in comparison to "long and obscure descriptions".[12]

The rationalisation movement at the end of the nineteenth century also reduced the diversity of things to a line. What engineer Frederick Winslow Taylor[13] started with tables in his time study work, Lillian and Frank Gilbreth continued with images, thus following the tradition of Marey. Likewise engineers, they were also preoccupied with recording traces of movement, but their focus was not the laws of nature rather the laws of the market. Through the study of the work habits of manufacturing and clerical employees in all sorts of industries, they looked for ways to increase output and make their jobs easier. They visualised workflows with photographic images of their observations. By comparing various images, small details came to the fore that formed the basis of their research.

For example, with their "Chronocyclegraph Motion Device",[14] the Gilbreths documented the movement paths of employees at work. The portrayed employee was covered with little light bulbs on points of his or her body that where significant to the movement path being studied. Through the use of long photographic exposure times, the movement was drawn as blurry lines by the dots of the light bulbs on the film negative. When the lighting was set in the right way, the person vanished completely from the picture and only the lines of the lights remained. These line structures could then be compared on the basis of equal parameters and accounted for differences that could optimise the workflow and increase efficiency. The different graphic structures that symbolise the paths of the worker were easy to understand, by employers as well as employees. Such a reduction to lines reflects a mindset to limit complexity for the benefit of demonstration and communication. Here, the line is the ideal means to achieve the most direct results.[15]

Coming back from simplification to complexity, the mathematician and philosopher Henri Poincaré offered a surprising explanation for the stability of the solar system in the 1880s. He wanted to demonstrate the path of the planets with a handful of mathematical functions. From the search for an "honest function", which in contrast to a monstrously large function should directly depict a theory of everything, resulted a theory for chaos physics. A contradiction caused the project to fail in describing the solar system with simplicity. His starting point made it necessary to reintegrate more and more of the previously reduced complexity. In a sense, "honest functions had run amok".[16] The hunt for a simple rule led to the insight that simplicity is only true in very specific cases. And in all his observations, he had trusted – more than logic – his intuition, which had called for a line. "I shall not even try to draw it," Poincare wrote, in view of the multitude of possibilities, but "[...] nothing is more suitable for providing us with an idea of the complex nature of the problem".[17] Neither the functions that should have led to simple laws nor the executed figures of the functions made it fully possible to represent complexity. Nevertheless, the graphic representations are needed to intuitively gain a glimpse into the understanding of complex structures.

Coding and Condensing

The process of coding and condensing is also very present in today's research work. The visual products of several sciences, with their size and/or speed, refer to "cut outs of the world". Through the application of instruments that should make the invisible visible, measurement data is produced in a first step, which is then collected and stored in computer memory. Often the result is an unmanageable amount of data that can only be dealt with by reducing the quantity. This can be achieved through visualisations. The selection of criteria from which these visualisations develop can be compared to the pre-digital drawing of a line – however, the human signature is hidden behind a machine. The process of reduction produces a clarity as well as a descriptive representation. The vividness of scientific imagery is attained through simplification, a process that makes the pile of data workable.[18]

Abstraction is used to generate comparable sets of data in order for something to be read from them. An analogous example can be found in the work of Johann Caspar Lavater, a priest and philosopher in the eighteenth century, who is known for his studies in physiognomy. His biography, interestingly enough, alternates between the arts and sciences (but in these times it wasn't so unusual and the distinction didn't weigh as heavily as it might today) as Lavater developed his "science" of reading faces by drawing portraits. He only drew the profile of the head of the portrayed person because the abstract contour served the purpose of his studies best. According to Lavater, this outline, on one hand, only represented half of the face; but on the other hand, this line is the most direct expression of nature – even the most talented portraitist is not capable of capturing it more precisely by hand. This line of the profile neglects all information about light, shadow, or movement and produces in its strict reduction the clearest testimonial of what the particular physiognomy *is* by nature. For Lavater, this line speaks for the quality of the face; but also moral and intellectual character can be read from it. With this method Lavater extended the normal practice of physical diagnostics of the time to the realm of the mind. In this sense, the face can be decoded and serves as a readable sign – or as Karl Pestalozzi points out in reaction to Lavater's achievements: the body is a text that signifies the soul.[19]

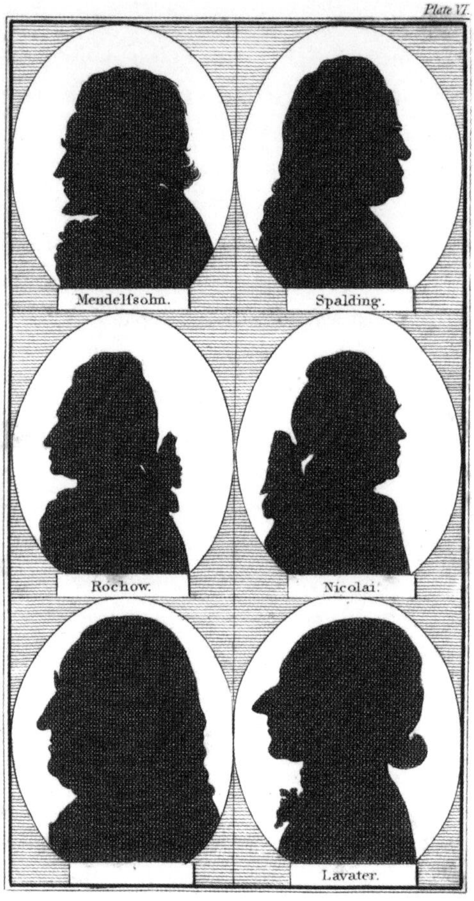

Fig. 4
From the technique of drawing the profile, Lavater obtains a line to be interpreted. He takes the measurements of his own profile and compares it with those of his colleagues. The simplicity of the method is also its advantage.

These decoding methods were deeply Eurocentric and were also happily employed by national socialist and fascist movements in the first half of the twentieth century because they also relied – like the visualised increase in efficiency – on simple basics: What becomes visible through abstract lines is also very easy to verbalise, for instance, whoever had a crooked mouth line, their mindset must also be so.
The British natural scientist Francis Galton, a researcher in the field of facial abstraction, established eugenics as a scientific discipline in the nineteenth century. In his search for stereotypical faces, his intention was not to make an abstraction of the individual face rather to condense many faces into one. For each stereotype category – for instance, the felon – he commissioned numerous photographic portraits on transparent paper. Each image was exposed on a photographic plate, one after the other, and a "composite image" was obtained through multiple exposure. The same exposure time was applied for every portrait, hence each image was equally represented in the final result. The photochemical process produced a composite network of lines that highlighted the most dominant features, thereby emphasising the typical characteristics of the stereotype. In this process, one also avoided the inaccuracy of the illustrator, who always includes a bias in the drawings. "A composite portrait," says Galton, "represents the picture that would rise before the mind's eye of a man who had the gift of pictorial imagination in an exalted degree. But the imaginative power even of the highest artists is far from precise, and is so apt to be biassed by special cases that may have struck their fancies, that no two artists agree in any of their typical forms."[20] Galton aimed to take abstraction out of the hands of the subjective artist and place it into the mechanical objectivity of an apparatus.

But also this objective production of lines can be understood as a way of "drawing lines" when one sees the camera as an extension of the pencil. That might sound a bit strange, but no one would disagree that it is the person doing the drawing who draws the line and not the pencil. On this note, it is fair to also question the hands and, above all, the heads behind the line-drawing machines and devices: Is someone who wrests an image from a computer tomograph a drawer?

Insight in Lines

These thoughts on the subjective mastery of lines and so-called objective automatic procedures lead back to the initial hypothesis that the line between art and science is a hard one to draw. The artistically drawn line implies a subjective supervision of the process, whereas the composed line of the machine is assigned a higher grade of validity. The belief in this differentiation is very common, but all lines together help to inspire intuition: They are signs but not explanations. And exactly here we find the true potential of the line: In all of its modesty, it opens a wide space for imagination and interpretation. The singular line or the network of lines functions as a signpost to ideas and possible explanations, whereby the referent of the line remains ambiguous. This vague element is often attributed to art as its kind of truth: the truth found in the quality of sensation. And this can be seen as an important part of human cognition, but in the form of a temporary truth, as an instantaneous *change* in cognition. In contrast, the scientific understanding of truth implies clarity and *consistency* in cognition.

Nevertheless, doesn't this retrospect on the history of the line in scientific and artistic contexts show that the difference between change and consistency is fluid and often more complementary than exclusive? The line by the machine is the continuation of a line that is drawn by hand and as such produces a sign, which presents us with a solution for many contingencies, but it is not an "honest function". In conclusion, can it be that a simple line represents our world as a complex system most efficiently?

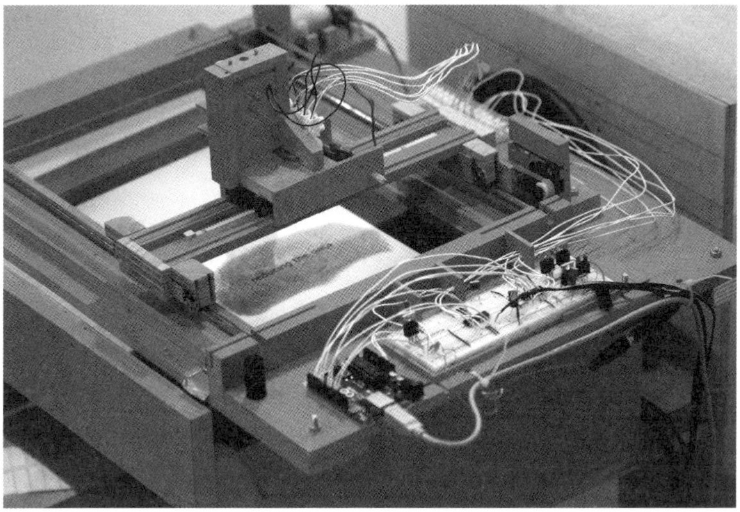

Fig. 5
Richard Schwarz, *Strichweise*, 2011

1
Novalis, *Philosophical Writings*, ed. and tr. Margaret Mahony Stoljar (New York: State University of New York, 1997), 23; Novalis, 'Blüthenstaub' in *Athenaeum No. 1* (Berlin: Frölich, 1798), 70.

2
Cf. Hans-Joachim Lenger, 'Einige Striche', in Katrin Sahner, *Zeichnen* (Hamburg: Textem Verlag, 2009), 122f.

3
Cf. George Spencer-Brown, *Laws of Form* (London: George Allen and Unwin Ltd., 1969; repr. Leipzig: Bohmeier, 2009), 3.

4
Lorraine Daston and Peter Galison, *Objectivity* (New York: Zone Books, 2007), 100.

5
William M. Ivins, *Prints and Visual Communication* (Cambridge, MA: Harvard University Press, 1953), 70.

6
Cf. Lorraine Daston and Peter Galison, *Objectivity*, 106.

7
Cf. Peter Assmann, 'Die Kunst der Linie – Anmerkungen zum Sichtbarmachen', in Peter Assmann (ed.), *Die Kunst der Linie. Möglichkeiten des Graphischen [Catalogue of the exhibition* Die Kunst der Linie – Möglichkeiten des Graphischen in *Landesgalerie Oberösterreich, 15.9.1999 – 9.1.2000]* (Weitra: Bibliothek der Provinz, 1999), 30.

8
Peter Galison, 'Images scatter into data, data gather into images', in Bruno Latour and Peter Weibel (eds.), *Iconoclash: Beyond the Image Wars in Science, Religion and Art.* (Cambridge, MA: MIT Press, 2002), 308.

9
Étienne-Jules Marey, 'Animal mechanism: A treatise on terrestrial and aerial locomotion', in *International Scientific Series*, 11 (1874; repr. New York: D. Appleton & Co, 1890), 27.

10
Marta Braun, *Picturing Time: The Work of Etienne-Jules Marey (1830-1904)* (Chicago: University of Chicago Press, 1992), 16.

11
Étienne-Jules Marey, 'Lectures on the Graphic Method in the Experimental Sciences, and its Special Application to Medicine' [Delivered at the Medical Congress in Brussels, 21 September 1875], *British Medical Journal*, 1/785 (1876), 66.

12
Ibid.

13
Frederick Winslow Taylor was highly influential for increased efficiency in the workflow. "Taylorism", a theory of management that is still controversial to this today, analyses production processes with the aim to economise time, resources (manpower), and unnecessary paths. At the time, a few similar ideas were coming up (cf. Henry Ford and the term "Fordism"), but Taylor would become the most popular representative of an economic practice that is also very applicable in contemporary information technology. Cf. Frederick Winslow Taylor, *The Principles of Scientific Management* (Norwood, MA: Plimpton Press, 1911).

14
Cf. Frank B. Gilbreth and Lillian M. Gilbreth, *Applied Motion Study. A Collection of Papers on the Efficient Method to Industrial Preparedness* (New York: Sturgis and Watson, 1917), 73–96.

15
Cf. Herbert Mehrtens, 'Bilder der Bewegung – Bewegung der Bilder', in Horst Bredekamp and Gabriele Werner (eds.), *Bildwelten des Wissen. Kunsthistorisches Jahrbuch für Bildkritik*, 1/1 (2003), 48.

16
Peter Galison, 'Images scatter into data, data gather into images', 303.

17
Henri Poincaré and Daniel L. Goroff, *New Methods of Celestial Mechanics*, vol. 3 (Woodbury, NY: American Institute of Physics, 1993 [1967/1899]), 1059; quoted in Peter Galison, 'Images scatter into data, data gather into images', 303.

18
Cf. Jörg Huber, 'Bilder zwischen Wissenschaft und Kunst. Eine Forschungsskizze', in Michael Egli (ed.), *Horizonte – Beiträge zu Kunst und Kunstwissenschaft* (Ostfildern-Ruit: Hatje Cantz, 2001), 384.

19
Cf. Gottfried Boehm, 'Mit durchdringendem Blick', in Michael Egli (ed.), *Horizonte – Beiträge zu Kunst und Kunstwissenschaft* (Ostfildern Ruit: Hatje Cantz, 2001), 83.

20
Francis Galton, *Inquiries into Human Faculty and its Development* (London: Macmillan, 1883), 343.

Fig. 2
Cf. Etienne-Jules Marey, *La méthode graphique dans les sciences expérimentales et principalement en physiologie et en médecine. Deuxième tirage augmenté d'un supplément sur le développement de la méthode graphique par la photographie* (Paris: G. Masson, 1885), 281.

Fig. 3
Jean-Baptiste Auguste Chauveau, Etienne-Jules Marey, 'Détermination graphique des rapports de la pulsation cardiaque avec les mouvements de l'oreillette et du ventricule obtenue au moyen d'un appareil enregistreur', in: *Comptes rendus des séances et mémoires de la Société de biologie*, 3/3 (1861), 7.

Fig. 4
Cf. Johann Caspar Lavater, *Physiognomy. The Corresponding Analogy between the Conformation of the Features and the Ruling Passions of the Mind* (London: Cowie, Low, and Co., 1826), plate VI, p. xxi.

The relentless urge to break things up, to look beyond the layers that appear as surfaces, to make visible the concealed processes and decisions that surround us. It leads me to question what we base our decisions on. Where do the consequences of our actions lead us, and the surrounding people and entities?

Relativisation of the social "divisions". These divisions are situated on the line of interpretation and objectivity, not always so…

Form an active part of a discussion and follow the discovered ontologies. Techniques of transfer and communication and interpretation. Form a coordination centre with collaboration. Important to exchange / welcome flux within our thought structures. This collaboration marks an important step in the approach to solutions for actual, future, real, or imagined problems.

I feel I am now preparing myself for research and work that may not have prescribed outcomes and will not judge itself entirely on original intentions, but allow itself to chart its own course and tell its own stories. "Engagement" is a word I would now use with the abandon I used "influence" with eight months ago, perhaps having acknowledged the presence of influence in many forms – instead of seeing an extraction of self for societal feedback, now considering the insertion of self.

How people from different areas are seen to be constructing their worlds, and the world that we are creating between and around these others. There is a question of service – with which entities are we involved and to whom do we answer, and what is in our service?

As a confessor of wisdom and freedom of thought, I am happy that we focus more on the philosophy of art than art itself.

The material and economic systems that govern us as much as we govern them are so deeply instilled in our world that their underlying purposes have been subverted and are no longer the driving factors of our decisions, made or unmade. Simultaneously, we come to a point where these underlying purposes may no longer serve us as they might have. Hyper-awareness exists enmeshed with deep embedment, and so, what of us and the worlds that will abide?

Promote complexity. Investigating hierarchies along with information flows and the rule of multidisciplinarity. The principle of "No Restrictions Experienced" fits into my research and work. Through project-based creation, inter- and transdisciplinary thinking and action are increasingly developed. New methods, approaches, and techniques become tools. Disciplinary foreignness and the connections between disciplines; ideas overlap disciplinary frameworks. The structural similarity of otherwise different disciplines. Transdisciplinary sharing of knowledge and strategies in research and art. Theoretical explorations of science. Human-focused artistic research with societal influences on interdisciplinary work. Finding and engaging with "warm" human influences and connection points in "cold" technical research. Static ideas and methods are not as good as dynamic ones. Bridge the thinks.

Sceptical about statements, advanced criticality, experiencing new ways to involve ourselves in discussions, and a slow digression from pure censuring and single pathways of thought. Permanent process of rethinking embedded in the chance of redoing. Sophisticated, freedom-based, and advanced field of study. Many layers and several directions to move. Multiple fields of research. Thinking on the creative process, and the verge between analogue and digital creation.

Appendix Index

12
Bruno Latour
An Attempt at a "Compositionist Manifesto"

60
Jour Fixe

62
Thomas Bugnyar
Raven Politics – Understanding and Use of Social Relationships

65
Valérie Pihet
Experiments on Arts and Politics

70
Nikolaus Gansterer
Figures of Research or
Harvesting the Tree of Knowledge

73
Victoria Vesna
Art|Science Collaborations: Being in Between

75
Oron Catts
Art Practice in the Form of "Tissue Culture"

80
Tom Holert
Joint Ventures. On the State of Collaboration

156
Johanna Schaffer
Artistic Re-re-research

216
Richard Schwarz
On Drawing Lines

Appendix Index

7
Preface

41
16 Images of the Week

88
Miscellaneous

- 90
  Theoretical Flotsam & Jetsam
- 94
  Research, Nature and History in a Museum
- 96
  Sabina Teichert
  Question – About Care
- 98
  Artists in a Lab
- 102
  The Essence
- 104
  Programming Workshop
- 110
  Martin Groedl
  SPAM
- 112
  Viennafair
- 116
  Blocking Street Cars and Horses
- 118
  Becoming an Art & Science Studio
- 122
  Powered by the Projector of Art & Science

126
Bernd Kraeftner et al.
Penser avec ~~(la chemise de)~~ Marcel

168
Catalogue of the exhibition *parameter{world} parameters for every or no thing*

210
Virgil Widrich
What do you do?

230
Gorilla Manifesto

Michael Bachhofer
Graduate in biology/ecology woth focus on ethnomedicine. He co-founded "FC-Mappers.net" and works as a freelance IT specialist. Student of Art & Science since 2010.http://FCMappers.net, http://MiB.FCMappers.net

Thomas Bugnyar
Born 1971 in Eisenstadt, received his PhD in biological sciences from the University of Vienna. After spending some time in the USA (Erwin Schrödinger fellow at University of Vermont) and in the UK (lecturer at University of St. Andrews), he returned to Vienna for the prestigious START programme of the Austrian Science Fund. He is now a professor for cognitive ethology and part of the newly founded Department of Cognitive Biology at the University of Vienna. His research focuses on social behaviour and complex cognition in non-human animals, ranging from social learning, perspective taking, and "theory of mind" to forms of cooperation and conflict management. He has published over 40 journal articles and is member of the editorial board of *Animal Behaviour*, the scientific committee of the Ethological Society, and the EU programme "Atomium Culture".

Pepa Bugueiro Domingo
Arrives in Vienna while living in Brussels and carrying eclectic works around in her natal Spain and Berlin. Graduated in product design engineering in Glasgow in 2009. Student of Art & Science since 2010. http://agence173.com/

Oron Catts
Is born in Finland, currently living and working in Western Australia. Artist, researcher, and curator. Co-founder and director of SymbioticA, The Centre of Excellence in Biological Arts, School of Anatomy and Human Biology, The University of Western Australia. Founder of the Tissue Culture & Art Project/TC&A (1996). Research fellow at the Tissue Engineering and Organ Fabrication Laboratory, Harvard Medical School (2000-2001). Trained in product design and specialised in the future interaction of design and biologically derived technologies. BA (First Class Honours) and MA in Visual Art.

Alin Cîrstea
Born 1987 in Lugoj, Romania. Bachelor degree in visual arts. Freelancer. Student of Art & Science since 2010. http://alincirstea.blogspot.com

Valerie Deifel
Studied theatre, film, and media studies and philosophy in Vienna. From 2007 to 2010, fellow at the Initiativkolleg "Senses, Technology, Mise-en-Scène: Media and Perception" at the University of Vienna. Since 2009, assistant in the master programme Art & Science at the University of Applied Arts Vienna. Works on a doctoral thesis on the blank space in film with focus on the aesthetics of experimental film.

Sarah Duit
Studied biotechnology and molecular biology in Vienna and worked on signal transduction and the establishment of neuronal structures in the development of the brain. During her studies, she became interested in the translations between science, visualisation, and art and decided to leave the laboratory bench in order to set out in this direction. Student of Art & Science since 2010.

Romana Egartner
Born 1985 in Villach. Studied at the University of Applied Arts Vienna, Department of Fine and Media Arts, Transmedia Art (Brigitte Kowanz), 2004–2010. Works as an artist in the fields of installation, video, animation, and photography. Exhibitions: "Lange Nacht der Musen", Klagenfurt, 2009; "Gemma Kunst schaun", Villach, 2010; "Radical Cartography – Mapping the Terminal" at the CAT Terminal Wien Mitte, 2010. Student of Art & Science since 2010.

Anna Fatér
Born in Budapest, began her art studies at Novus Art College film and video class, completed her bachelor degree in drawing and visual communication at the Art University of Kaposvár. Interested in film, drawing, and animation. Student of Art & Science since 2010.

Rudolf Friemel
Received his BA at FH Joanneum in Graz (information design). Works as a graphic artist and user interface designer. Student of Art & Science since 2010.

Nikolaus Gansterer
Born 1974, lives and works in Vienna and Berlin. He studied transmedia art at the University of Applied Arts Vienna and finished his postgraduate studies at the Jan van Eyck Academy in Maastricht. He co-founded the Institute for

Transacoustic Research and the Vegetable Orchestra. Since 2007, he has been a lecturer at the University of Applied Arts. In his visual work Gansterer focuses on mapping processes emerging out of cultural and scientific networks, unfolding their immanent structures of interconnectedness. Recent presentations of his work include: "Living and Working in Vienna II", Kunsthalle Wien, Vienna; "Sonar Festival", CCCB, Barcelona; "Moving Patterns", ACF, New York; "Architecture of Interaction", Chisenhale Gallery, London; "Hard Rock Walzer", Villa Manin, Udine; "Wrong time, Wrong place", Tent, Rotterdam; "The Stone Road", Argos, Brussels; "Structures", Transmediale, Berlin; "Sound Escapes", Space Gallery, London; "Mifan", AnniArt Gallery, Beijing, and "Story behold. Story be told", Kunsthistorisches Museum, Vienna.

Michaela Grass
From an apprenticeship as a gardener (Bundesgärten Schönbrunn, Vienna) through technical communication engineering (College for Technology, Schellinggasse Vienna) to textile and interior design (The University of Derby, England). Lives and works most of the time in Vienna as a projectionist and for studies and has a great interest in film. Student of Art & Science since 2010.

Martin Leopold Groedl
Born 1983. Studies in philosopy, media, and informatics in Vienna. Freelancer in web/software development and interactive installations. Works in generative art and automatic drawing. Student of Art & Science since 2009.

Juliana Herrero
Born 1975 in Argentina. Studied architecture in Buenos Aires and was the assistant of Prof. Alberto Varas. 2004 postgraduate degree in conceptual design (under Prof. Ben van Berkel) at the Staedelschule, Frankfurt am Main. From 2004 to 2005, participant in the film class of Prof. Mark Leckey, Frankfurt am Main. Various competitions and exhibitions in the fields of architecture, art, and spatial design with related film works and publications. Since January 2010, assistant in the master programme Art & Science at the University of Applied Arts Vienna.

Tom Holert
Born 1962, is an art historian, critic, curator, and artist. A former editor of *Texte zur Kunst* and *Spex*, he currently lives and works in Berlin and is a honorary professor at the Academy of Fine Arts Vienna, where he has held (until September 2011) the chair of Epistemology and Methodology of Art Production. At the academy, he co-coordinated the Center for Art/Knowledge, the PhD in Practice, and the WWTF Art(s) and Science project "Troubling Research". Alongside his writings on contemporary and late modernist art, Holert (co-)authored books on visual culture, politics, war, mobility, glamour, and the governmentality of the present – amongst them *Fliehkraft. Gesellschaft in Bewegung – von Migranten und Touristen* (with Mark Terkessidis, Kiepenheuer and Witsch, 2006), *Marc Camille Chaimowicz. Celebration? Realife* (Afterall/MIT Press, 2007), *Regieren im Bildraum* (b_books/Polypen, 2008), *Das Erziehungsbild. Zur visuellen Kultur des Pädagogischen* (ed., with Marion von Osten, Schlebrügge Editor, 2010). As an artist, Holert recently participated in "Mimétisme" (Extra City, Antwerp, 2007), "Manifesta 7" (Trento, 2008), "Fake or Feint" (Berlin, 2009), "Modernologies" (MACBA, Barcelona, 2009 and Museum of Modern Art in Warsaw, 2010), 8th Gwangju Biennale 2010, and "Forum Expanded" (Berlin International Film Festival, 2011).

Ashley Holwell
Born 1986 in Whangarei, New Zealand. Works as a furniture designer and artist between Rotterdam and Vienna. Currently studying while creating design work as Studio Bread. Previously exhibited: "we still will", Auckland, 2008; "De Nieuw Oogst", Rotterdam, 2010. Student of Art & Science since 2010.

Anna Fríða Jónsdóttir
Visual artist and photographer from Iceland. She completed her BA in fine arts at the Iceland Academy of the Arts in 2010. In her works she has focused on the relationship between the dream world and the perceived world, looking for answers to myths and the paranormal in science. Student of Art & Science since 2010.
http://www.annafrida.com

Bernd Kraeftner
Born near Lake Constance, Austria. He studied medicine and worked as a filmmaker and author. Since 1998, he has been exploring the messy interfaces between science and society. He was principal investigator of various transdisciplinary research projects funded by the Austrian Ministry of Science; the Wellcome Trust's SciArt

initiative, London; the Center for Art and Media, Karlsruhe; the Humboldt University, Berlin; the Austrian Science Foundation (FWF); the Vienna Science and Technology Fund (WWTF). He co-curated the science exhibition "the true/false.inc" in Vienna (2006). As founding member of the "Research Centre for Shared Incompetence", he investigates method development in science(s) and art, transdisciplinarity, science and technology studies, and the arts. http://sharedinc.net

Bruno Latour
Born 1947 in Beaune, Burgundy, from a wine grower family, was trained first as a philosopher and then an anthropologist. From 1982 to 2006, he was a professor at the Centre de Sociologie de l'Innovation at the École Nationale Supérieure des Mines in Paris and, for various periods, visiting professor at UCSD, at the London School of Economics, and in the History of Science Department of Harvard University. He is now a professor at Sciences Po Paris where he has also been the vice-director and scientific director since 2007. Together with Peter Weibel, he curated the exhibition "Iconoclash: Beyond the Image Wars in Science, Religion and Art" (ZKM, 2002) and "Making Things Public. The Atmospheres of Democracy" (ZKM, 2005). He published, amongst others, *Laboratory Life* (with Steve Woolgar, 1979), *Science in Action* (1987), and *We have never been modern* (1993).

Michal Marencik
Born in Skalica, Slovakia. Former student of fine arts, philosophy, and interactive media in Brno. Works in the fields of video, interactive installations, sculpture, sound art, experimental music + performance art, photography, and screenprint graphics. Student of Art & Science since 2010.

Iulian Moise
Since 1993, working in televisions, then for different film or graphic design companies. He graduated from the Fine Arts Faculty of Timisoara, a beautiful city in the Banat region of Romania. Student of Art & Science since 2010. http://www.wix.com/julianmoisse/visual

David Palme
Lives and studies in Vienna. Bachelor degree in computer studies. Works as a freelance graphic designer. Student of Art & Science since 2010.

Valérie Pihet
Was the assistant of Bruno Latour from 2002 to 2005. She was partly in charge of the coordination of the exhibition "Iconoclash. Beyond the Image Wars in Science, Religion and Art" (ZKM, 2002). She was also responsible for the coordination and setting up the exhibition "Making Things Public. Atmospheres of Democracy" (ZKM, 2005). From 2005 to 2007, she developed collaborations with organisations that cross arts and new media and with various artists and scientists (Pierre Huyghe, Adam Lowe, Thierry Fournier, Luc Boltanski). At the end of 2007, she joined Bruno Latour at Sciences Po, Paris. From 2007 to 2010, she was the project manager for the implementation of the médialab at Sciences Po. The médialab is a laboratory of digital resources with the mission to contribute to renewal in research in social sciences and in its sources, working methods, and the manner in which it deals with its objects. Since 2011, she has been the executive director of the Master of Experiments on Arts and Politics programme at Sciences Po.

Leon Ploszczanski
Born 1981 in Vienna. Studied zoology in Vienna and Marseille. Lives and works in Vienna. Graduated from Art & Science Visualization in 2011.

Johanna Schaffer
Researches, teaches, and translates in the areas of visual culture and material aesthetics with a queer-feminist, anti-racist focus. At the Academy of Fine Arts Vienna, she is part of the team that has developed and runs the PhD in Practice programme. She is also involved in "Troubling Research. Performing Knowledge in the Arts", a collaborative research project amongst nine artists and theorists on the historical, ideological, and institutional conditions of artistic research as a concept and as contemporary practice. For recent publications, see Barbara Paul and Johanna Schaffer (eds.), *Mehr(wert) queer – Queer Added (Value). Visuelle Kultur, Kunst und Gender-Politiken – Visual Culture, Art, and Gender Politics.* (Bielefeld: transcript, 2009); and Johanna Schaffer, *Ambivalenzen der Sichtbarkeit. Arbeit an den Strukturen der Anerkennung.* (Bielefeld: transcript, 2008).

Waltraud Schartmüller
Diploma in conservation sciences at the University of Applied Arts Vienna. Student of Art & Science since 2009.

Richard Schwarz
Born 1984. Studied European ethnology in Innsbruck – therefore interested in almost everything. Graduated from Art & Science Visualization in 2011.
http://www.islandrabe.com

Wolfgang Schwarzenbrunner
Studied multimedia art in Salzburg and biomedical engineering in Vienna. Student of Art & Science since 2009.

Manuel Stark
Bachelor of arts in information and media design at the HfG Schwäbisch Gmünd. Worked for several design agencies, now working as a freelancer. Lives and studies in Vienna. Student of Art & Science since 2010.

Sabina Teichert
Lives and works in Vienna. Studied at the University of Visual Arts, Darmstadt and University of Fine Arts, New York (Fulbright-Scholarship). Student of Art & Science since 2009.

Beniamin Urbanek
Born in Cracow. Interested in modelling and animation. Lives, works, and studies in Vienna. Student of Art & Science since 2009. http://beniaminsmonster.bplaced.com

Victoria Vesna
Is a media artist and professor at the UCLA Department of Design | Media Arts and director of the Art|Sci Center at the School of the Arts and the California Nanosystems Institute (CNSI). She is currently a visiting professor at the School of Art, Media, and Technology at Parsons The New School for Design in New York, a senior researcher at IMéRA – Institut Méditerranéen de Recherches Avancées in Marseille, France, and artist in residence at the Institute of Advanced Studies, University of Bristol. Her work can be defined as experimental creative research that resides between disciplines and technologies. With her installations she explores how communication technologies affect collective behaviour and how perceptions of identity shift in relation to scientific innovation. Victoria has exhibited her work in over twenty solo exhibitions and more than seventy group shows, has been published in excess of twenty papers, and gave 100+ invited talks in the last decade. She is the North American editor of AI & Society, and in 2007 she published the edited volume *Database Aesthetics: Art in the Age of Information Overflow*, Minnesota Press. Recently published is *Context Providers: Conditions of Meaning*.

Andrea Weidlich
Diploma and doctoral degree in computer science. Graduated from Art & Science Visualization in 2011.

Virgil Widrich
Born 1967 in Salzburg, has worked on numerous films and multimedia productions. His first feature film for cinema *Heller als der Mond* ("Brighter than the Moon", 2000) received several awards and his short film *Copy Shop* won 35 international awards and was nominated for an Academy Award. His short *Fast Film* won 36 international awards, has to date been shown at 285 festivals, and in 2006 was included in the list of the 100 most important short films of the past 100 years by 30 leading film critics at the Annecy Animation Festival. From 2007 to 2010, he was a university professor of digital art at the University of the Applied Arts Vienna; since 2010, he has been leading the master programme Art & Science at the same university.

Brigitte Zwick
Born 1971 in Feldkirch. Studied nutrition science in Vienna, specialised on the antibacterial effect of essential oils used as food additives. Educational activity on healthy nutrition. Student of Art & Science since 2009.

Acknowledgements

Thank you for permission, production, and other assistance to: Annie Ochmanek (Artforum); Shannon Jackson (Johns Hopkins University Press); Mark Markin (Paul Kasmin Gallery); Melinda Lee (SLAC National Accelerator Laboratory); Gerry Shaw (EnCor Biotechnology Inc.); Christoph Offenberg and Margarita Diaz (Sony Pictures Entertainment); Timm Hartman (Van Laack); Margret Ziska (Der Spiegel); Hans Hemmert; Walton Ford; Svenja Kratz (SymbioticA); Josef Penninger and Arabella Meixner (IMBA); Christian Koeberl and Reinhard Golebiowski (Museum of Natural History Vienna); Angela Fössl (Springer); Daniel Breyer and Gerlinde Kugler (Holzhausen); Sonja Orman, Georg Glaeser, Alfred Vendl, Anja Seipenbusch, and Rector Gerald Bast (University of Applied Arts).

We would like to give special thanks to all collaborators on this book: Thomas Bugnyar, Oron Catts, Nikolaus Gansterer, Tom Holert, Bruno Latour, Katja Mayer, Valérie Pihet, Johanna Schaffer, Victoria Vesna, Michael Bachhofer, Alin Cîrstea, Sarah Duit, Romana Egartner, Anna Fatér, Rudolf Friemel, Michaela Grass, Martin Groedl, Juliana Herrero, Ashley Holwell, Anna Fríða Jónsdóttir, Michal Marencik, Iulian Moise, Leon Ploszczanski, Waltraud Schartmüller, Richard Schwarz, Wolfgang Schwarzenbrunner, Manuel Stark, Sabina Teichert, Beniamin Urbanek, Andrea Weidlich, Brigitte Zwick, Peter Blakeney, Christine Schöffler, Pepa Bugueiro Domingo, and David Palme.

Thanks to all (other) guest speakers at the Art & Science department from 2009 to 2011 for the inspiring talks and discussions: Ulrike Exner, Judith Fegerl, Martin Füllsack, Michael Hieslmair, Kurt Hofstetter, Roman Kirschner, Herwig Kopp, Renate Quehenberger, Friederike Range, Martin Reinhart, Gabi Schillig, Markus Schmidt, Karl Stocker, Alexander Wilkie, and Michael Zinganel.

Photo credits

If not stated otherwise, the copyright of the image is by the author or the image is used in terms of academic quoting.

46: Digital still ©1963, renewed 1991 Columbia Pictures Industries, Inc. All Rights Reserved. Courtesy of Columbia Pictures; 49: Image courtesy and copyright ddp images/AP/Chinatopix; 51: ©2011 VBK, Vienna; 52: Georg Hochmuth / picturedesk.com; 56: ©2011 The M.C. Escher Company-Holland. All rights reserved. www.mcescher.com; 60: ©2011 Valerie Deifel, Pepa Bugueiro Domingo; 65: ©Thomas Bugnyar; 68–69: Screenshot of http://speap.sciences-po.fr ©Baldinger•Vu-Huu + Blumbyte Webdesign; 72: Nikolaus Gansterer, *Translecture*, 2009, ©Nikolaus Gansterer; 74: James Gimzewski, Victoria Vesna, *Zero@wavefunction*, 2002, ©Victoria Vesna; 79: Oron Catts, Ionat Zurr, *The Semi-Living Worry Dolls*, 2011 (Exhibition *synth-ethic*, Natural History Museum Vienna, 14 May–26 June 2011), ©Sabina Teichert; 90–93: Seminar by Bernd Kraeftner, ©2010 Sabina Teichert; 94–95: Museum of Natural History Vienna ©2011 Iulian Moise; 96–97: ©2011 Sabina Teichert; 98–101: Workshop "Biotechnology and Contemporary Art" by Svenja Kratz, Institute for Molecular Biotechnology (IMBA), Vienna (9–15 May 2011), ©Manuel Stark; 102–103: *The Essence*, MAK Vienna (29 June–17 July 2011) ©Juliana Herrero; 102 bottom: Leon Ploszczanski, *Eine galvanische Reise*, 2011; 103 top: Richard Schwarz, *Strichweise*, 2011; 103 bottom: Ashley Holwell & Romana Egartner, *We went on a Data Quest…*, 2011; 104–108: Processing Workshop by Martin Groedl, poster design: Martin Groedl, Beniamin Urbanek; 112–115: Viennafair, Vienna (12–15 May 2011), stand design: Juliana Herrero, ©Sabina Teichert; 116–117: Window modification: Juliana Herrero, ©2010 David Palme; 118–123: ©2010/2011 Pepa Bugueiro Domingo, Alin Cîrstea, Juliana Herrero, Iulian Moise, David Palme; 118–119: Furniture design: Ashley Holwell; 134 left: ©Pepa Bugueiro Domingo; 134 right: ©Martin Groedl; 135: ©Brigitte Zwick; 136 left: ©Alin Cîrstea; 136 right: ©David Palme; 137 left: ©Sabina Teichert; 137 right: ©Rudolf Friemel; 138 left: ©Anna Fríða Jónsdóttir; 138 right: ©Iulian Moise; 139: ©Manuel Stark; 140 left: ©Michaela Grass; 140 right: ©Wolfgang Schwarzenbrunner; 141 left: ©Romana Egartner; 141 right: ©Anna Fatér; 142 left: ©Michal Marencik; 142 right: ©Sarah Duit; 143 left: ©Michael Bachhofer; 143 right: ©Waltraud Schartmüller; 144 left: ©Ashley Holwell; 144 right: ©Richard Schwarz; 145: ©Leon Ploszczanski; 154: ©2011 VBK, Vienna; 168–208: Image design of catalogue: Sabina Teichert; photos: Sabina Teichert, Rudolf Friemel, Iulian Moise, Virgil Widrich, and the artists; 170–171: ©Anna Fatér, Manuel Stark, *Manimal Project*, 2011; 172–173: ©Brigitte Zwick, *Excretor vs Nonexcretor*, 2011; 174–175: ©Rudolf Friemel, *Intertwined Viennese Lines*, 2011; 176–177: ©Pepa Bugueiro Domingo, Michal Marencik, *Sector 33A*, 2011; 178–179: ©Richard Schwarz, *Maps like Face(s)*, 2011; 180–181: ©Sabina Teichert, *High Beta 21–38Hz*, 2011; 182–183: ©Anna Fríða Jónsdóttir, *Thought Interpreter*, 2011; 184–185: ©Alin Cîrstea, *Invader*, 2011; 186–187: ©Alin Cîrstea, Michaela Grass, *Untitled Process (Working Title)*, 2011; 188–189: ©Beniamin Urbanek, *Some Monters*, 2011; 190–191: ©Martin Groedl, *Egograms Series*, 2011; 192–193: ©Romana Egartner, Ashley Holwell, *Kinetic Meta*, 2011; 194–195: ©Romana Egartner, Ashley Holwell, *We went on a Data Quest…*, 2011; 196–197: ©Michael Bachhofer, David Palme, *Brunnenmarkt Dynamics*, 2011; 198–199: ©Sarah Duit, Iulian Moise, *Musicteria*, 2011; 200–201: ©Leon Ploszczanski, *96.4% Copper*, 2011; 202–203: © Wolfgang Schwarzenbrunner, *I'm Covered with the Blood of Jesus*, 2011; 204–205: ©Andrea Weidlich, *The Emperor's New Clothes*, 2011; 206–207: ©Sabina Teichert; 212 bottom: ©Hieronymus Bosch or Pieter Bruegel the Elder, *Beggars and Cripples*, between 1465 and 1559 ©Bibliotheque Royale Albert I, Brussels; 215 bottom: ©Iulian Moise; 227: ©Juliana Herrero; 230: Poster of Walton Ford, *An Encounter with Du Chaillu*, 2009, watercolour, gouache, pencil, and ink on paper, 242.6 x 152.4 cm ©Walton Ford, Courtesy of Paul Kasmin Gallery, New York.